EXMOOR'S
Industrial Archaeology

EXMOOR'S
Industrial Archaeology

Edited by
Michael Atkinson

EXMOOR BOOKS

First published in 1997 by Exmoor Books

British Library Cataloguing in Publication Data
A CIP catalogue record for this book is available from The British Library

ISBN 0 86183 318 X

Exmoor Books is a partnership between the
Exmoor Press and Exmoor National Park Authority

Trade sales enquiries to:
HALSGROVE
Halsgrove House
Lower Moor Way
Tiverton EX16 6SS
Tel: 01884 243242
Fax: 01884 243325

Printed in Great Britain by Bookcraft, Midsomer Norton.

CONTENTS

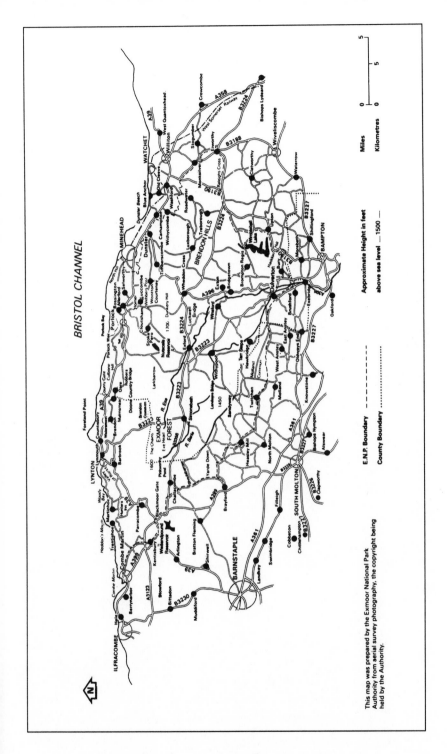

BRISTOL CHANNEL

This map was prepared by the Exmoor National Park
Authority from aerial survey photography, the copyright being
held by the Authority.

E.N.P. Boundary — — — —

County Boundary ....

Approximate Height in feet
above sea level —1500 —

Miles   0   5
Kilometres 0   5

7

GENERAL EDITOR'S PREFACE

This volume owes its conception to a symposium on the Industrial Archaeology of Exmoor held by Exmoor National Park Authority and the Centre for South-Western Historical Studies in May 1992. Before that symposium had become even a twinkle in the eye of its begetters, several committed industrial historians and archaeologists had devoted a great deal of time and skill to research and fieldwork on the unique rural industrial complexes of Exmoor. At the symposium, different aspects of industrial archaeology were brought together and have coalesced in the formation of the Exmoor Mines Research Group and the decision to produce a book based upon the symposium and other current research.

The appointment of an archaeologist to the staff of the National Park Authority in 1991 emphasised its commitment to the encouragement of field-work and research designed to build a fuller picture of past human presence and activity on Exmoor. Industrial history and archaeology are integral parts of a rich pattern of human exploitation which is etched upon and embodied in the landscape of Exmoor. We welcome and support the Exmoor Mines Research Group and are glad to assist in the publication of this volume.

The manifold themes of industrial Exmoor, from mining to wool processing, are brought together here in one volume for the first time. The varied and colourful styles of the authors reflect the diversity of their subjects and their own professional backgrounds, producing a veritable mine of information and animating the text with their enthusiasm. An essential product of all archaeological research is the public availability of results and conclusions. This book is intended to inform and to interpret and to share with a wider public the enjoyment of understanding the evolution of Exmoor's historic landscape.

Veryan Heal

INTRODUCTION

Mick Atkinson

> The gaunt chimneys, the ugly pumping-houses, do not improve a land-
> scape already rendered sufficiently dreary by the rows of ruinous cot-
> tages bordering the roadside... silence now reigns where, a dozen years
> since, the air resounded with the cheerful, if not always melodious, voice
> of commerce.

In these words written in 1893, John Lloyd Warden Page described the demise
of the once prosperous Brendon Hills mines and settlement. The same scene of
abandoned industry was repeated, though not on the same scale, at various
locations on Exmoor such as Combe Martin, Heasley Mill and Simonsbath.

To many people and especially the visitor to Exmoor, the area seems to be one
of rural beauty altered only by Man's striving to eke out a living by farming the
unforgiving uplands. Yet, the curious traveller cannot fail to notice the remains
of past industrial activity which evidence a rather different past. Exmoor has
been the source of valuable raw materials such as copper, lead, silver and iron
ores and quarried stone. The wool from its sheep and the power of its rushing
streams gave rise to a textile trade whilst a number of other small industries
arose providing goods and materials to local industry, agriculture and the population at large.

Sadly, many of the physical remains of past economic activity have disappeared but sufficient is left to be preserved for posterity as a monument to those
who toiled on the moor or risked their capital in ventures which too often
ended in failure. It is probably just in time that some serious surveys and
preservation work are now under way.

The range of industries which existed on Exmoor was small and predominantly primary. The largest employer was probably the woollen textile trade
but, in the main, these workers did not toil in large mills of the type associated
with the Lancashire and Yorkshire trades from the late eighteenth century but
in houses, farms and small fulling mills, so the industry did not present an
'industrial' exterior. It was woven into the fabric of a rural, largely agricultural
society, providing an opportunity for gainful second occupations for many.

The most important 'true' industry was the metalliferous mining industry,
which therefore dominates this volume. How important it was over the centuries is impossible to ascertain as there are few records available prior to the

1850s to give historians the means to calculate its value as profitable enterprise or employer of labour. The true worth of such nationally significant operations as medieval silver mining at Combe Martin or eighteenth-century copper mining at North Molton will probably never be known.

In many ways, Exmoor must be viewed as a marginal economic area, with limited natural resources, an isolated and difficult terrain which made the all-important transport and communications links awkward to establish and maintain, poor soils and a scant population. In common with the rest of the South West peninsula, it had no local supplies of coal and therefore rarely smelted the metallic ores which it produced. The minerals it possessed were, with a few exceptions, not present in sufficient quantities to rank the area amongst the major producing areas and the mining industry in particular suffered from intermittent production as mines opened and closed as the prices of metals rose and fell.

However, Exmoor does have the advantage of a coastline bordering on the Bristol Channel and, despite the difficulty of constructing adequate harbours, was therefore able to make use of coastal shipping, for a long time the cheapest form of transporting goods. Opposite and easily visible on clear days lies South Wales and the Bristol Channel, regarded now as a barrier to trade and a nuisance to the traveller, was a thoroughfare for traffic between these two interdependent regions. From the early eighteenth century, South Wales was the destination of nearly all the ores produced in the South West, together with Bristol during the heyday of the brass industry. This was particularly true for the iron ore trade during the period 1830 to 1880, with Exmoor sending all of its ores there and, as will be seen, forming the basis of dreams of huge iron ore wealth which never materialised. Other cross-channel links included the export of copper ores to Bristol, the Wye valley and Swansea and the importation of limestone to the Exmoor kilns and a certain amount of coal for steam engines. The basic reason for this export of ores to be smelted elsewhere was the lack of coal in the South West as a whole, coupled with the fact that, until the second half of the nineteenth century, the production of metals took more fuel than ore so it made more sense to transport ore to fuel than vice versa. For those who treasure the beauty of Exmoor, it is a frightening thought that by the 1850s it was beginning to make more sense to take the coal to the ore source and, had Frederic Knight succeeded in finding the large iron ore deposits he was searching for, Porlock Bay would probably have been transformed into a Barrow-in-Furness or Middlesbrough.

As well as an extractive-industries based export trade, there was a range of trades and industries which existed for the local market. Quarrying was one such industry with stone being used for local building and roadmaking, and even the more specialist slate quarry at Treborough supplied a predominantly

11

local market with roofing slates, cisterns etc., probably because of its inferior quality. Before the railways created national markets and regional specialisations, most areas and particularly more isolated ones, produced many of their own requirements and the Exmoor region was no exception. Thus, the area supported wheelwrights, millwrights, agricultural machinery makers, tanners, sawyers, millers etc. The textile and paper trades were more thoroughly linked to outside areas both for supplies and markets but were still dependent to a certain degree on local demand.

Crucial to practically all of these industries was transportation. Adequate roads and bridges were needed to facilitate the movement of wool, yarn and cloth to the various domestic processing sites (farmsteads and houses), whilst, despite the advantage of proximity of coastal transport for metallic ores and limestone, most enterprises involved in the bulky trades such as iron ore, stone and lime realised that cheap transport was central to their success. Just as Dartmoor was penetrated by tramways driven from the edge of the moor to take away clays, peat or stone, so Exmoor was too or would have been. Most famous was the Brendon Hills mineral railway, but there were also schemes for transporting limestone and iron to and from the Royal Forest which came to nought and the Florence Tramway which served iron ore mines.

This volume draws together years of research and fieldwork by experts in their fields with the aim of making the general public more aware of Exmoor's industrial past. It is not the final word on the subject because a lot of work is in progress or remains to be done and space does not allow greater detail, but hopefully this will form a basis and a catalyst for future efforts. Each chapter covers the history, technology and remains of the industry with varying emphasis depending on what is known or remains of each industry. Whilst our hope is that more people will become interested in the old moor industries and perhaps set off on investigative walks, rides or drives, it must be remembered that many of the sites mentioned are on private land and permission must be sought before entry. It must also be remembered that mines and quarries are by their nature holes in the ground which can be dangerous. Never enter a mine entrance without adequate equipment and expertise and always be vigilant with children and pets because even the smallest working can cause injury or worse.

The stimulus for this volume came from the Exmoor National Park which organised the symposium which brought together researchers who had never before gathered together as one body with one expressed interest and who realised that there was a public demand for more knowledge of this previously under-publicised aspect of the history of Exmoor. The National Park authorities have begun the process of protecting Exmoor's industrial heritage just in time, with such initiatives as the Burrow Farm engine house conservation, information boards and extensive site surveys. The positive approach of the Park to the industrial archaeology of Exmoor gives rise to a greater sense of confidence that the relics to be seen today will be seen by our great grandchildren.

IRON MINING

Mike Jones

Geology, Mining and Smelting to 1800

The rocks of Exmoor belong to the Devonian system and are formed of compacted alternating marine and continental sediments, principally sandstones and slates. As a result of pressure from the south acting upon them, the slates have been subjected to folding and cleavage, the cleavage dip being south at about 70 degrees below horizontal As mineralisation appears to be closely associated with the fold axes, the lodes strike generally in five lines in echelon oriented about 13-16 degrees north-west of an east-west line. The ores are lenticular in nature and in discontinuous pockets connected by barren clay. The south walls of the lodes are often separated from the adjoining slates by a vein of quartz. At surface the slates enclosing the ore bodies are grey, but at depth blue-green. In addition to their southerly dip, the ore pockets slope in a westerly direction along the line of their strike, and on Exmoor itself the lodes tend to pinch out and die away at depth, as well as being more discontinuous than those on the Brendon Hills to the east.

Two specimens of ore, one from Exmoor and one from the Brendon Hills, were included among an international selection shown in the Geological Section of the Great Exhibition of 1851. Subsequently all the minerals exhibited were given to the Museum of Practical Geology where the 130 specimens of British ores were analysed by one of the leading metallurgists of the time, John Percy F.R.S. He found that the Brendon Hills specimen contained about 35% of iron, but that in the case of the Exmoor specimen 'the proportion of iron was so small (about 14%) that the ore would more properly be designated "ferriferous limestone".' Unusually for British ores both samples had only the slightest trace of phosphoric acid, a fact that was later to be of great significance.

The metallurgy of iron is generally thought to have developed in Anatolia in about 2000 BC and to have spread in waves to other regions at intervals several centuries apart. Although the technology arrived in Britain between the fourth and sixth centuries BC, it may not have reached Exmoor until a couple of centuries later. At this time ore was not 'mined' as the term is now understood, but was extracted by trenching on the outcrop of the lodes. Traces of these 'openwork trenches' may still be seen, most spectacularly at SS 7538 near Cornham Ford on Exmoor, and until the early years of the twentieth century others were visible at several places on the Brendon Hills and at Crowbarn Hill near North Molton. The openwork near Cornham Ford is about 700yd (600m.) long and although much infilled, up to 26ft (8m.) deep in places. Originally it was more than 50ft (15m.) deep as was demonstrated when a shaft was sunk through it in the 1850s. On the Brendon Hills a core drilling made in 1961 into the former openwork at Burrow Farm (ST 008345), indicated an original depth of about 46ft (14m.) at that place.

The method of winning the ore was to sink a shaft on to the outcrop of the lode until the ingress of water became too great, when a new shaft would be sunk a few metres farther along the outcrop, a 'pillar' of ground being left between the two. Later most of the pillars were removed to create long trenches, with sides that were inclined to follow the dip of the lode. The over-hanging south side of the trench is known as the 'hanging wall', and the north side the 'foot wall'. 'Mining' was on a very small scale and was carried on inter-mittently, enough ore being removed for an annual 'campaign' of smelting in the winter months to furnish trade goods and tools for the following year. Ore production can hardly have exceeded 10-20 tons a year from the whole of Exmoor, and, because of the wasteful smelting process employed, the yield of finished iron was in the order of 1 ton per year. The openworks cannot be dated, but their extent and the tiny production figure postulated above suggest that they were first opened in the second or third century BC and only fell into disuse in the late Middle Ages when the enclosure of the hills gathered pace and the complexities of land tenure meant that opencast working on a casual basis was no longer possible.

Until the Middle Ages iron ore was smelted locally by the 'direct process' in very small quantities, using charcoal as fuel, first in shallow pits and later in open hearths utilising natural draught or man-powered bellows. The tempera-ture achieved was insufficient to melt the iron, but was enough to reduce it to a malleable lump which was hammered to expel the slag. Amounts smelted by this process were of the order of 11-18lb (5-8kg) at each melt. A significant increase in production was achieved in the fifteenth century by the application of water power to blow the furnace, and in some of the larger smelting houses, for the operation of the hammer. The introduction of this new technology had the effect of concentrating production at a few sites where a constant water supply could be relied upon. It was at these sites that 'bloomeries' were estab-lished, comprising a bowl furnace about 1ft (0.3m.) deep and 1ft 7in. (0.5m.) in diameter, equipped with large leather bellows to provide the air necessary for the reduction of the ore to malleable iron. In spite of the increase in blast, tem-peratures sufficiently high to reduce the ore to a molten state were rarely achieved, and the slag still had to be driven out by hammering. Nevertheless it was then possible to produce 55-110lb (25-50kg) of iron in twelve hours on a regular basis.

As charcoal is ground to useless powder when transported, iron ore was taken for smelting by packhorse to the wooded valleys which border Exmoor. Quantities of iron slag, probably derived from the primitive smelting processes described above, have been recorded at several sites, notably Aldworthy near Eisen Hill (SS 9037), Syndercombe near Clatworthy (ST 0330), and at Sherracombe Ford on the southern edge of Exmoor (SS 7136). It is possible that this site was a water-powered bloomery, and it may be that there was another at Bridgetown (SS 9233) where a bloom large enough to be cut into two parts was ploughed up in a field nearby in 1862. There is a reference to an 'iron mill' at Horner (SS 8945) which was said to have worked from 1600-1610.[1] This too may have been a water-powered bloomery, but it is just possible that it was a charcoal blast furnace and forge, as the 'indirect' smelting process had already reached South Wales twenty or thirty years earlier.

Nineteenth Century Mining

The Brendon Hills

The origins of nineteenth-century mining on Exmoor may best be understood in the wider context of the iron industry of South Wales. By the first decade of the nineteenth century the 'indirect' process of smelting iron ore in large coke-fired blast furnaces using limestone as flux had become well established, and South Wales was by this date one of the principal fully industrialised areas of the United Kingdom. The table below well illustrates not only the astonishing increase in South Wales iron production per se, but, until the mid 1830s, the increase as a proportion of the national production of iron.

Year	Numbers of furnaces S. Wales	U.K.	Output in '000 tons S. Wales	U.K.	Percentage increase S. Wales	U.K.	S. Wales furnaces as % age of U.K.	S. Wales output as % age of U.K.	Year
1806	45	216	68	250	–	–	21	27	1806
1823	72	266	182	455	168	82	27	40	1823
1830	113	333	278	677	52	49	34	41	1830
1840	163	508	505	1396	82	106	32	36	1840
1848	196	626	631	2100	25	50	31	30	1848
1855	187	761	840	3200	33	52	25	26	1855
1860	200	852	969	3800	15	19	23	25	1860
1870	184	916	979	5600	1	47	20	17	1870
1880	141	926	890	7749	-9	38	15	11	1880

Iron production in South Wales as a proportion of national production 1806-80

The table also shows the significant deterioration in South Wales' position after 1840. This resulted from two causes: technical progress and an increasing scarcity of high quality iron ore. The introduction of heated blast air for the furnaces by Neilson in Scotland in 1828 was quickly taken up by other ironmaking areas. Output increased markedly at first, but in South Wales there were insufficient raw materials of high quality to sustain the increase. The customary method of mining for ore in South Wales was by 'patching', a form of opencast strip mining of easily accessible but low-grade ores. By the 1830s these ores were becoming exhausted and deep mines had to be sunk, causing production costs to rise sharply. It became imperative to find new sources of ore which would be competitive in price and quality with the locally mined ore.

It was particularly unfortunate for the South Wales' ironmasters that this crisis occurred at this time, for the opening in 1830 of the Liverpool & Manchester railway initiated the railway age, which created enormous demands for wrought iron rails, products which the Welsh ironmasters found especially profitable. Each mile of track required about 80 tons of rails, and the rapid increase in railway construction fuelled a demand greater than the existing industry could meet. Investors seeking high returns on their capital were attracted to South Wales, and new or reconstructed ironworks began to come into production. Not all were soundly managed, and as there was a tendency on the part of investors to judge the soundness of a concern by the composition of the board of directors, it is hardly surprising that many firms foundered. This was especiallly unfortunate because of the tendency for investors in one firm to be drawn from a relatively small geographical area. One example of such a concern was the Pentwyn ironworks near Pontypool which had originally been established in the 1820s. One of its principal shareholders was Sir Thomas Lethbridge of Bishops Lydeard in Somerset. He was then in his forties and came of an old Cornish family; Sir John, his father, had been created a baronet in 1804 for assisting in the relief of the Prince of Wales' pecuniary difficulties and for contributing to John Luttrell's expenses in the 1802 Minehead election. He had died in 1815, leaving Sir Thomas with estates and capital to invest. Sir Thomas was for more than twenty years M.P. for Somerset, and Colonel of the 2nd Somerset Militia, and had a town house in the Royal Crescent in Bath.

The Pentwyn ironworks was quite a small concern, but after 1830 the directors decided to expand. In 1838 the company was restructured as the Pentwyn & Golynos Iron Co., with offices, not surprisingly at Bath, and directors who were drawn mainly from north Somerset and Wells. In 1837 the old company had contracted to supply the Warsaw-Vienna Railway with 14,000 tons of rails, which would have required an entire annual production of this works, and for which the company were to have been paid 1500 '4% Original Shares' in the railway, a not uncommon arrangement, but one which placed considerable financial risks and burdens on the supplier. After the delivery of a small part of the order, the contract was cancelled and the agreement finally annulled in 1841.[2]

Perhaps the management of the Pentwyn works was inefficient or their technology outmoded, for without apparently severing his connection with the company, Sir Thomas decided to take a major share in an ironworks to be built on a greenfield site. In August 1836, he and some of the directors of the Pentwyn company, together with the chairman and two of the directors of the Bath & Weymouth & Great Western Union Railway, a company which disappeared without trace shortly afterwards, were among nine provisional directors of the Monmouthshire Iron & Coal Company. The company prospectus, issued in October 1836, showed the authorised capital as £300,000 on which a return of 32% was anticipated. In the prospectus the directors drew investors' attention to their ownership of collieries at Abercarne which could furnish ample supplies of the best coking coal which would not only be used for smelting, but would be 'exported' to Somerset, Devon and Cornwall in exchange for supplies of ore from those counties. Here is an early acknowledgement of the inadequacy of Welsh ore supplies.

In fact such a trade had been in existence for some time, as the Ebbw Vale Company had been obtaining quantities of ore from mines at Brixham on the south Devon coast, and had been sending back cargoes of coal in part payment. Thus was Sir Thomas awakened to the possibility of obtaining ore from his own Somerset estate, over part of which, particularly in the parishes of Luxborough and Withiel Florey on the Brendon Hills, the long disused openwork mine trenches lay. In the autumn of 1837, therefore, Sir Thomas engaged one of the Pentwyn Company's advisers, A. Morrison, a mining geologist of Pontypool, to advise him how best to proceed. Morrison visited the Brendon Hills, inspected the openworks and took samples of ore for analysis.

Meanwhile the Monmouthshire Iron Company's start up was not going well. The directors had decided to build three blast furnaces, 150 workers' dwellings, a truck shop and school on land owned by Sir Benjamin Hall, about 2 miles south of Ebbw Vale. The new town was named Victoria in honour of the new queen. The project manager was Roger Hopkins, a civil and railway engineer, and under him were 770 company employees. The economic situation was unfavourable, many shareholders had difficulty meeting calls, and the directors were forced to borrow £18,000 to enable work to continue on site. Finally on 1 January 1839, the furnaces at Victoria were blown in and the company could at last begin to produce iron 'in which quality is of more importance than quantity'.

Almost at once the unfavourable economic situation deteriorated into a slump, which the company, with only £54,485 capital paid up, was not strong enough to weather. With large quantities of unsold iron on hand, the company was wound up. In 1840 it was reformed with substantially the same directors, but the successor company fared no better and, the price of iron having fallen by 50%, the works were assigned to the Monmouthshire & Glamorgan Banking Co. in lieu of repayment of a £12,000 debt, and assisted by Robert Mushet, the noted ironmaster of the Forest of Dean, the bank attempted to keep the works going. The bank were unable to make the works pay, and the furnaces and buildings reverted to the ground landlord.

In spite of, or perhaps because of, these setbacks, Lethbridge was determined to open mines on his Brendon Hills estate, but the principal difficulty to be overcome was finding a means of transporting the ore to the coast for shipment to Wales. In January 1839, Sir Thomas sought permission from a neighbour, the 4th Earl of Egremont, who had a country estate at Williton, to lay down a tram-road from Watchet to the Brendon Hills for conveyance of the ore. As Sir Thomas expected the Earl to give him the land on which to lay the tramroad, negotiations soon ground to a halt. To surmount this difficulty Sir Thomas decided to construct a 'smelting furnace' on his own land in Luxborough, and in November 1840 a progress report appeared in the *Taunton Courier*, giving an exaggerated account of the scope and extent of the 'iron mill'. What Sir Thomas seems in fact to have constructed was a charcoal bloomsmithy, a technological step back into the previous century. The exact location of this bloomery is unknown, but it is likely that it was at SS 974359 about 220yd (200m.) north of the entrance to the adit of his mine, in Chargot Wood.

In April 1841 the first of a long series of advertisements appeared in the *Mining Journal* offering to let the mine and 'furnace'. The advertisements continued intermittently until Sir Thomas' death in 1849. The only taker was Robert Mushet, who wrote for details of the lease in 1846 but, as he later stated, 'the lease was so hampered with heavy royalties and endless clauses that I would not entertain it.' With Sir Thomas' death his family's interest in exploiting the ores of the Brendon Hills came to an end.

In 1846 Smith Tibbits and his brother William, both from Cornwall, knowing of the copper mines in the North Molton area, and perhaps being aware of the impending opening of Wheal Eliza copper mine near Simonsbath, considered that copper would also be found on the Brendons. They obtained a licence from Sir Thomas Lethbridge and in that year began driving a level north from SS 966351 on Gupworthy Farm, looking for copper. A shortage of working capital delayed progress and it was two years before they encountered a splendid lode, nearly six metres thick, but of iron ore not copper. Mushet later described Tibbits as a 'grazier', but whether this was intended in the literal sense, or whether in the sense of someone who makes a discovery and then moves elsewhere is not clear. In any event the difficulties of transport and sale had to be overcome before the discovery could be exploited. Tibbits sent trial loads of ore to the Tredegar and Dowlais ironworks, but it was found to deaden the blast furnaces because of the large quantities of carbon dioxide produced during its smelting, and after several attempts to deal with it, when it was christened 'Tibby's ore', the ironworks declined to take more. Tibbits later claimed to have lost £2000 by the venture, and moved on to Wootton Courtenay, near his home at Dunster, where he worked opencast iron mines at Brockwell.

At about this time Samuel Blackwell the Dudley ironmaster who, in a lecture in 1851 had suggested the exploitation of the Northamptonshire ores, obtained the specimens of ore from Sir Thomas' Chargot Wood mine and from Wheal Eliza on Exmoor for the Great Exhibition. Realising the potential of the Brendon Hills ores but lacking the capital to work them himself, he passed the information to his thirty-four-year-old brother-in-law, Ebenezer Rogers of Abercarne in South Wales, who formed the Brendon Hills Mining Company early in 1852. The company obtained licences from the principal landowners to search for ore and continued Tibbits' work at Gupworthy and sank a new shaft through the former openwork trenches at ST 025342 at Brendon Hill. Finding a rich lode there, the working was named the Raleighs Cross mine. Having proved to his satisfaction the nature and extent of the lodes, Rogers attempted to interest the Ebbw Vale Company in his discovery.

The Ebbw Vale ironworks had first been established in 1790 and by 1796 was owned by the Harford family who were also Bristol bankers. In 1818 they bought Sirhowy ironworks two miles to the west, as well as several collieries; in 1820 they opened a forge, puddling furnaces and rolling mills at Ebbw Vale where in 1835 they are said to have rolled rails for the Stockton & Darlington railway. Hot blast was introduced about 1832 and the company prospered steadily until 1842 when the banking division suffered heavy losses on loans made to the southern states of the USA, and the Ebbw Vale Company was forced into liquidation. The works were kept going by trustees until they were bought in 1844 for £216,000 by a group of Midlands industrialists headed by Abraham Darby of Coalbrookdale. One of the partners was Thomas Brown who acted as works manager at Ebbw Vale. His father had been a Worcestershire ironworker who moved to Penydarren works at Merthyr Tydfil in 1786: in 1811 he set up wrought iron bar mills at Nantyglo and on his death his two sons Thomas and James became works managers at the Blaina and Cwmcelyn works. In 1848 Brown was responsible for the purchase by the company of the Victoria ironworks; he was rather cautious in his dealings, but encouraged technical progress. In 1849 he introduced the use of coke ovens, he encouraged the development of the works laboratory and was largely responsible for increasing the output of furnaces from 100 to 150 tons per week. In 1852 the company bought the Abersychan works near Pontypool, and in 1860 acquired rights to important opencast ore fields near Bilbao in Spain. He retired in 1861.

After initial hesitation, the Ebbw Vale partners decided to develop the Brendon Hills mines and appointed Thomas Brown to oversee their development. In 1853 the partners bought out Rogers and took over his licences and leases upon payment to him of an annuity of £1000 for the next sixty years. The Ebbw Vale partners formed the Brendon Hills Iron Ore Company and under Brown's direction, began the work of serious exploitation and development. The problem of transporting the ore to Watchet for shipment to Newport was uppermost in their minds, and the account of the mineral railway constructed to solve the problem is covered elsewhere in this volume.

The partners lost no time in obtaining leases of mining rights over the whole length of the Brendon Hills and Eisen Hill to the west of the Quarme valley, and David Richard of Tredegar was appointed mines captain. He continued shaft sinking at Raleighs Cross and turned headings on to the lode at Gupworthy, where in 1857 a steam powered rock drill was at work in the adit, although without any great success. In 1855, the first year for which official mineral statistics were produced, more than 4000 tons of ore were produced, which increased in the following year to about 5000 tons. Adits were driven into the hill at several places, especially in Chargot Wood near Sir Thomas' old mine, which had been abandoned by this time, and at Kennisham Hill at SS 969359. At Eisen Hill (SS 9037 and 9137), adits were driven west and east into the lode and proved to be very productive.

The iron ores of Exmoor and the Brendon Hills, as has been noted, were almost free from phosphoric acid. Generally they were spathic iron ore, that is iron carbonates, although near the the surface they had weathered to oxides, haematites. In August 1856 Henry Bessemer read a paper entitled 'On the manufacture of malleable iron and steel without fuel' to the British Association for the Advancement of Science at the Queens Hotel, Cheltenham, having been persuaded to do so by George Rennie. Until then steel had been manufactured in very small quantities in crucibles and was considered almost a precious metal. It was much stronger, harder and had greater elasticity than wrought iron and Bessemer's announcement that he had found the means of making it in large quantities simply by blowing air through a vessel filled with molten iron caused an immediate sensation.

Thomas Brown carried out laboratory trials of the process at Ebbw Vale and at once discovered that the steel made by Bessemer's process was 'red short' and of no value. He referred the problem to his friend R. F. Mushet who remelted Brown's sample, and added to it 'spiegeleisen' (a compound of iron, manganese and carbon) and thus produced excellent steel. Brown then offered to buy the patent rights from Bessemer for £50,000, but Bessemer preferred to issue licences for the use of the process from which he expected ultimately to earn more. It was not long before the other licensees discovered the defects in

21

Bessemer's process and it took Bessemer and other metallurgists more than two years to discover the cause and to find a remedy. The cause was the phosphorus normally found in iron made from British ores, which by chance had been absent from the iron that Bessemer used in his experiments. Non-phosphoric ores, such as that from the Brendons, were now sought after by potential steelmakers, and the fact that by the early 1860s the Ebbw Vale Company had installed Bessemer converters and were beginning to roll steel rails in quantity placed them in a position of commercial advantage. The works increased their demand for ore, and the mines captain was instructed to spare no expense in completing the railway and developing the mines.

In 1858 David Richard had died and was succeeded by Morgan Morgans who was not only mines captain but project engineer on the railway as well. Under his direction the railway was extended west to Gupworthy, workers' houses at Brendon Hill and Gupworthy were constructed, and ore production increased to a peak of 36,000 tons in 1864. In 1865 a 50in. (127cm.) beam pumping engine was installed at Raleighs Cross mine and two years later the mine was over 380ft (116m.) deep with 17 levels east and west from the engine drift. Carnarvon New pit (ST 021342) was sunk in 1866 when the old pit 200yd (180m.) to the east , ran out of the ore because of the westward slant of the ore body. Level 10 of the new pit was connected to level 13 of the Raleighs Cross mine by means of a winze.

At Gupworthy, working ore through the level was so inconvenient that Morgans 'sunk' a drift upwards from the adit to the surface at SS 967353 close to the railway, and installed a pumping and winding engine there. By 1867 the main drift was 260ft (79m.) deep with 10 levels. Because this was beginning to run out of the ore a westward divergent branch of the main drift was sunk, and was then 310ft (94m.) deep. Five years later this too began to run out of the ore, and an entirely new drift known as Gupworthy New pit was sunk 440yd (400m.) to the west.

After a promising start, the mines on Eisen Hill proved disappointing and by 1861 were hardly being worked. Until then they had not been under Morgans' control, but in that year he was given responsibility for them and under his management production increased markedly. Because of their distance from the railway, ore from the Eisen Hill mines was taken by road to Minehead and shipped from there, but following the increased production in 1862-3, it was decided to extend the railway down to the Quarme valley. Because of the huge costs involved, this proposal for an eight mile long steeply graded adhesion worked line was immediately abandoned. In the event ore production from the Eisen Hill mines fell quickly after Morgans left in 1867, and ten years later they were all but abandoned.

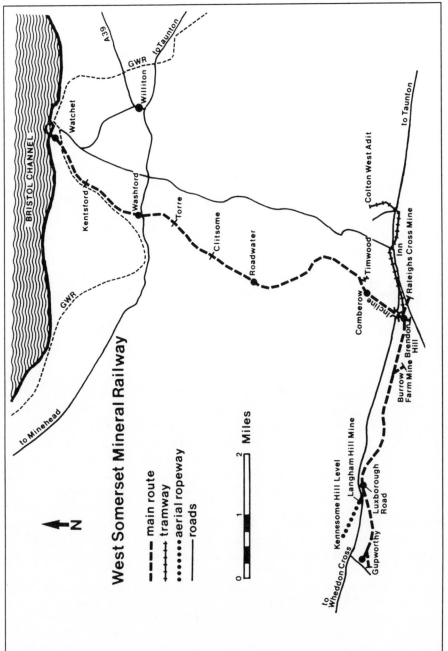

The Brendon Hills mines and railways.

Three levels in Chargot Wood had produced several thousand tons of ore by the end of 1865. This was wound up to a railway siding at Langham Hill by a narrow gauge incline worked by horse whim. In 1866 the sinking of a shaft at Langham Hill at SS 977356, was started in order to unite several of these smaller workings, and a combined pumping and winding engine was installed at surface. By 1874 the shaft was almost 700ft (213m.) deep, but work there ceased soon after. Close by was the terminus of an aerial ropeway from Kennisham Hill adit half a mile (1km.) to the west by means of which ore was brought to the siding at Langham Hill.

Kennisham Hill adit was driven south into the hill from SS 969359, and when it reached the lode turned west on to it. After driving 656yd (600m.) it became inconvenient to bring ore out of the adit, and a shaft was sunk at SS 963361 and a 28in. (71.1cm.) Cornish beam engine was installed for pumping and winding. The shaft here reached a depth of 468ft (142m.) with seven levels below the original water adit. Later, ore was taken from the shaft to the rail terminus at Gupworthy by a horse drawn tramway 550yd (500m.) long, and the aerial ropeway dismantled.

At Colton (ST 055348) an adit was driven west into the hill in 1865 and after driving 130ft (40m.) ancient workings were intercepted about 100ft (30m.) below ground. Between 1872-4 a second adit was driven into the hill from the west. Shafts were sunk on to both adits, but the ore was patchy and work was abandoned about 1876. Ore was taken to Brendon Hill by road for loading on to the railway.

Among the smaller mines, Burrow Farm at ST 008345, was sunk first in the early 1860s, and a portable engine installed; the skip shaft was 150 feet (45m.) deep by 1867, but the mine seems to have closed soon after. A few years later it was reopened and a 26 in. (66cm.) Cornish beam pumping and winding engine installed, the house for which is the only standing relic of these mines, having recently been conserved by Exmoor National Park. The mine continued working until the general closure of all the mines in September 1883.

Because of the lack of proper railway and port facilities in northern Spain, the exploitation by the Ebbw Vale Company of their opencast workings there did not get under way until after 1865 when the first railway was opened. Imports of Spanish ore only assumed significance after 1871 when four British companies were newly registered to mine Spanish ore, followed by eight more in 1872. By the end of 1875, 22 British companies had been floated to meet the demand for Spanish ore.

In 1872 the Carlist rising against the Spanish government severely disrupted the shipment of ore from Bilbao. By the summer of 1873 the uprising had gained strength, Bilbao was besieged by Carlist forces for ten months, and all commerce was suspended. Only in May 1876 was the insurrection brought to an end. In 1871 400,000 tons of ore had been exported from Bilbao, but by 1882 this had increased tenfold. Of this total 3 million tons came to Great Britain.

Morgans resigned as mines captain on the Brendons in 1867 and set up a consultancy in Bristol. His place was taken by Henry Skewis who had been captain of Crane mine in Cornwall. Due to a recession in the steel industry the price of ore fell sharply at this time, from 10/- a ton which it had been for the previous ten years, to 5/8d. in 1869, rising to 7/- in 1870. Output was cut back accordingly, from 32,000 tons in 1867 to 14,000 tons in 1870, but as the demand for Bessemer steel picked up in the early '70s, production was increased to reach a peak of almost 47,000 tons in 1877. Nevertheless there was a prolonged recession in the steel industry during the 1870s, and the Ebbw Vale Company were making increased trading losses, which by 1877 amounted to £677,000.

The conclusion of the Carlist uprising in 1876 and the consequent increase in imports of cheaper Spanish ore resulted in the closure of the some of the smaller and less productive mines on the Brendons. By 1879 competition from Spanish haematite became irresistible, and with one week's notice the mines were closed. A public subscription was opened to assist those miners who could not obtain work locally or in Cornwall to move to the lead mines of the north of England for work. After six months trade revived a little, and the mines were reopened on a reduced scale.

In that year the Gilchrist-Thomas modification of the Bessemer process, whereby the lining of the converter was changed to dolomite, was successfully launched. This allowed steel to be made from phosphoric ores as well as from those that were free from this impurity. Brendon Hills ore no longer had any advantage over any other ore, and as it was dearer than Spanish ore, there was no reason for the Ebbw Vale Company to continue to mine it. Notice to surrender the mining leases was given in August 1882 to take effect a year later. All machinery and movable parts of buildings such as doors , windows and roofing slates were sold and the hamlets of Brendon Hill and Gupworthy, and all the mines abandoned.

The great storm that ravaged the southern half of England in December 1900 destroyed much of Watchet harbour and most of the vessels sheltering within it. Repairs were started in 1903 under the direction of H. Blomfield Smith a civil engineer experienced in harbour work. The derelict mines interested him, and as the demand for ore was increasing and its price rising, he decided to reopen them. On 11 March 1907 the Somerset Mineral Syndicate was formed with Blomfield Smith as managing director. The syndicate leased the railway as far as Brendon Hill and cleared out both adits at Colton from where a 2 ft narrow gauge tramway was laid alongside the public road to take ore to the top of the incline at Brendon Hill. The ore from Colton was too crumbly for use in the blast furnaces, tending to clog, and the syndicate had great difficulty in selling it. Accordingly an attempt to reach the Raleighs Cross mine at depth was made by means of a 1100yd (1000m.) long adit driven south west from near Timwood (ST 032352), but before this reached half way to the Raleighs Cross mine, the syndicate was experiencing financial difficulty.

In an attempt to keep going and to sell the considerable quantities of ore being brought out of Colton pit, the syndicate decided to make the crumbly ore into blocks which would retain their integrity in the blast furnace. The Watchet Briquetting Syndicate was formed in 1909 and built a crude block-making plant at ST 048411 beside the Mineral Railway at Washford station, and an Osman kiln in which the blocks were to be fired was constructed nearby. During this time a slump in the steel trade had caused the closure of the Ebbw Vale furnaces for twenty weeks in 1908-9, and although a trial load of 80 tons of blocks was sent over in November 1909, both syndicates were insolvent and winding up orders were obtained in April 1910.

While the Mineral Syndicate were at work, a Liverpool-based group were trying to reopen Elworthy (Yeanon) pit at ST 064334. The shaft was cleared down to 60yd (55m.), and a pump installed in March 1907, but the project seems to have been abandoned without any ore being raised.

These were the last serious mining operations to be carried out on the Brendon Hills.

Exmoor

Shortly after buying the Forest of Exmoor in 1818 John Knight paid £762 for the mineral rights which had been reserved to the Crown. As an ironmaster himself, he would have been aware of their potential value, but as far as is known he made no attempt to exploit them. The first recorded iron mining on Exmoor began in 1846 when Wheal Eliza mine, about a mile south east of Simonsbath at SS 785381, which had possibly been worked in the sixteenth century, was opened by a group of businessmen from South Molton, although the principal shareholder in the venture was a Tavistock surgeon. The venturers in Wheal Eliza undertook to keep at least six miners at work and to pay Knight one fifteenth share of the ore raised. After 200 tons of ore had been raised, the lessees were required to build six cottages at the site. By May 1846 the lode had been uncovered at the surface and an adit driven into it from the north bank of the River Barle, and a shaft sunk on to it about 110yd (100m.) away. By August the shaft was 24ft (7.3m.) deep and the captain recommended the installation of a water wheel for pumping and winding. The wheel was completed in May 1847 and shaft sinking recommenced.

Only a few lumps of copper ore were ever recovered in spite of further shaft sinking, driving of cross-cuts, and the discovery of a second lode. The cottages were built, together with blacksmith's and carpenter's shops, but the copper ore raised did not repay the outlay and work was suspended in October 1849. Following a further injection of capital, work was restarted in the following year and the mine struggled on. Early in 1852 a rich pocket of ore was found but this quickly petered out and in spite of the discovery in March 1854 of a promising lode half a mile to the south, all work ceased in June 1855.

Knight's son and successor, Frederic, realised that although as a copper mine Wheal Eliza was a failure, there was sufficient iron ore in the mine to make its acquisition a sound venture. Through a nominee he bought the unexpired portion of the lease and the cottages with fittings, and all the mine machinery, for £328. He does not seem to have worked the mine, but it was included in the lease that he granted in April 1856 to Schneider and Hannay.

Knight took a keen interest in the development of the Brendon Hills mines, and invited Blackwell and Rogers to Exmoor to advise him about Exmoor's mineral potential. Hoping to repeat their success of a year or so before, Blackwell and Rogers sank a shaft on one of the lodes that had been exposed by trenching at SS 762378, near Blue Gate at the south west corner of the old Deer Park. In 1854 62 tons of ore were raised and sent for smelting to Blackwell's ironworks at Dudley. Trials were made in other areas of Exmoor in that year: at Hangley Cleave (SS 7436), Burcombe (SS 7438 and 7538), and at Picked Stones (SS 7937). Early in 1855 Knight commissioned a report from William Llewellyn a mining geologist from Pontypool, with a view to persuading South Wales iron firms to develop the Exmoor iron mining field. Llewellyn's report was enthusiastic and advised the development of that part of the Forest lying south of the Exford-Challacombe road, before undertaking work on the ground to the north of that road.

Armed with Llewellyn's report Knight persuaded the Dowlais Company of Merthyr Tydfil to visit Exmoor in October 1855. They too were impressed, but were concerned about the problems of transporting ore to the coast for shipment. After some discussion it was agreed that the Dowlais Company would lease an area of about 9 square kilometres lying astride the Simonsbath-South Molton road and extending as far as Kinsford Gate (but excluding the Deer Park where Rogers had made his trials) for forty-two years, in return for which they would pay a dead rent and 1/- (5p.) a ton royalty. In addition the Company agreed to supply Knight with sufficient rails and the winding machinery for inclined planes to facilitate the construction of a railway from Exmoor to Porlock provided Knight formed the earthworks and actually constructed the

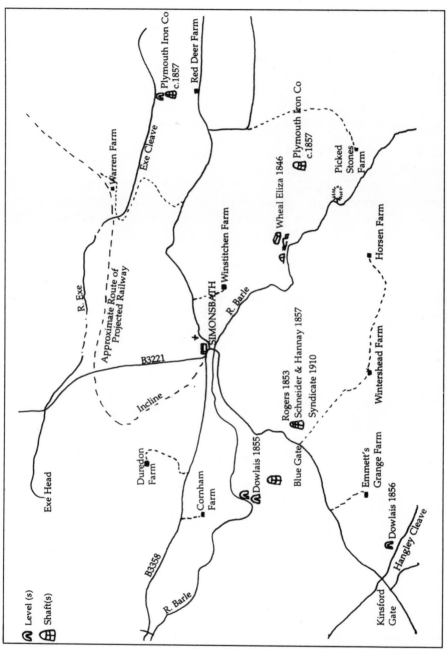

Mining operations around Simonsbath in the nineteenth century.

Level (s)

Shaft(s)

Exe Head

R. Exe

R. Barle

B3358

Duredon Farm

Cornham Farm

Dowlais 1855

Blue Gate

Rogers 1853

Schneider & Hannay 1857

Syndicate 1910

Emmett's Grange Farm

Dowlais 1856

Hangley Cleave

Kinsford Gate

SIMONSBATH

Winstitchen Farm

R. Barle

B3221

Incline

Approximate Route of Projected Railway

Warren Farm

Exe Cleave

Plymouth Iron Co c.1857

Red Deer Farm

Wheal Eliza 1846

Plymouth Iron Co c.1857

Picked Stones Farm

Horsen Farm

Wintershead Farm

line. The cost of the ironwork was to be charged at trade price and offset against royalties due from the lessees. The Dowlais Company began to mine by open-work trench south from Cornham Ford in November 1855 but after raising only 175 tons the lode petered out and work at this site was abandoned in June 1856.

During this time a start was made with driving levels south from the Cornham Ford area (SS 749387) in order to prove the lie and extent of the lodes, but after two and a half years of work, no worthwhile quantities of ore had been recovered. Other levels were driven in the Burcombe valley in further attempts to find the lodes, but although iron ore was found it was too intermixed with quartz to be of value. Nevertheless, 1856 was seen as a year of great promise by the Dowlais Company, and there is no doubt that they prosecuted the search for the lodes with vigour. Unfortunately, all they found was the clay track on the lode; their findings showed that on their sett at least, ore did not exist in work-able commercial quantity. In 1856 an adit was started, at SS 744367, to connect with Rogers' trial shaft at Hangley Cleave, but after bringing out 1200 tons of ore at considerable expense the trial was abandoned in the summer of 1857.

Another firm who were apparently anxious to secure supplies of ore was the Lancashire partnership of Schneider and Hannay. Henry Schneider had arrived in the Furness district of Lancashire in 1839 as a speculator and dealer in met-alliferous ores and soon built up a reputation for a degree of astuteness, ambi-tion and self-interest which bordered on the dishonest; indeed although he had been M.P. for Norwich from 1857-60, his election in that year was declared void on the grounds of corrupt electoral practices. In partnership with Robert Hannay he was responsible for the development of the Ulverston iron ore field, the construction of the Furness railway and the formation of the port of Barrow-in-Furness. In 1850 Schneider had discovered the Park mine, 'the second great-est haematite ore deposit in British history' (the first was Hodbarrow, also near Barrow-in-Furness), and by 1856 it was producing about 120,000 tons of ore a year, much of which was shipped to the Dowlais Company in South Wales.

It is hardly surprising therefore, that Schneider was anxious to secure for himself a lease on Exmoor, even if it was only to prevent others from doing so, and in 1856 Schneider and Hannay agreed to lease a large tract of Exmoor not already included in leases to others, including the Wheal Eliza mine, still fully equipped. The partners agreed to pay a dead rent of £2000 a year, and royalties of 1/3d. (6p.) per ton for ore and 8d. (3p.) a ton for clay ironstone. In addition the partners offered to contribute £7000 towards the cost of the railway to the coast, hardly generous considering the likely cost of the railway would have been in excess of £100,000.

The partners began by deepening Rogers' shaft near Blue Gate and installing a portable steam engine for pumping and winding. They also seem to have driven a trial adit in the area SS 741430. After a year's work only 800 tons of ore had been raised, and the partners considered that there was no ore capable of being worked at a profit. They gave Knight notice of their intention to surrender their lease, and withdrew early in 1857. Knight took the view that Schneider and Hannay had not given mining a fair trial and began a Chancery suit against them. Judgement was given in Knight's favour, but rather than go through with the action in the Queens Bench, Schneider paid Knight £10,000 as an out of court settlement.

In January 1857 Knight granted a lease, on the same terms and for the same period as the Schneider & Hannay lease, to Anthony Hill of the Plymouth Iron Company, whose ironworks were a mile or so south of Merthyr Tydfil. The dead rent was £500 a year, and the lessee covenanted to drive adits or sink shafts to a depth of at least 100 feet (30.5m.) below the surface. The area leased to the Plymouth Company was 1000 acres (404.6 hectares) and included part of Winstitchen Farm, most of Honeymead, Picked Stones and Warren Farm to the north of the Exford-Simonsbath road. The company began work on Picked Stones farm by sinking a shaft in the area (SS 798377) about 330yd (300m.) east of White Water. They also seem to have started driving a level from White Water to the shaft and another a few yards east of the shaft, but neither seems to have progressed very far (Burton, 1989, p.144). North of the Exford-Simonsbath road, the company drove a level south from SS 809400 and sank a shaft on to it about 35 metres from the portal; it is said that 500 tons of spathic ore was taken out of this mine in 1858. The Plymouth Company also started to drive an adit in a northerly direction from Sparcombe Water (SS 817409) but abandoned it after about 30 yards. In spite of Knight's hopes that they would enlarge their taking after the withdrawal of Schneider and Hannay, the Plymouth Company too gave notice of surrender of their lease which took effect in 1859.

The iron trade in England and Wales underwent a period of depression in 1857-8, when the price of ore fell below 10/- (50p.) a ton, and the Dowlais Company were tempted to abandon operations on Exmoor. Their captain on Exmoor, Henry Scale, gave such encouraging reports of progress that the company decided to continue the search, but such was the fickle nature of the lodes that every encouraging discovery was almost at once succeeded by disappointment. Even the withdrawal of Schneider and Hannay failed to discourage the Dowlais Company; indeed the feeling amongst the other participants was that Schneider and Hannay were not interested in mining, but rather in preventing others from doing so, in order that demand for ore from their Park mine would be maintained in a time of depression. The depression of 1857-8 caused a cessation of work by the Dowlais Company for fifteen weeks and in March 1858, the company gave twelve months' notice of terminating their agreement. Their captain, Henry Scale, was replaced by William Dunstan, who had been in charge of Wheal Eliza when it was being mined for copper, and who had been employed by Rogers to sink the trial shaft at the Deer Park in 1854. After that he had been employed at the Combe Martin iron mine and now returned to Exmoor determined to make a success of it. The results of the operations in 1858 gave no cause for encouragement, and in June the Dowlais Company commissioned an independent report from Stephen Eddy and John Taylor, which resulted in the termination of all work on Exmoor. The Dowlais Company wrote a long letter to Frederic Knight setting out the record of their sincere endeavours to find ore and asking for 'the measure of liberality usually accorded, under such circumstances, to mineral tenants'. Knight, however generously disposed to the Dowlais Company he may have been, was fettered by a Chancery suit in which he was involved with his brothers and sisters. After further negotiations, Knight initiated proceedings against the Dowlais Company in 1859, to require them to fulfil their obligations in respect of the provision of rails and ironwork for the railway to the coast. The matter was finally settled in 1862 when the Dowlais Company agreed to pay Knight £7000 in lieu of the rails, etc., handing over to Knight all mining plant and machinery then on the moor.

After an abortive attempt at about the turn of the century to recommence mining on the moor, the next significant development took place in 1908. In that year Henry Roberts of West Bromwich sought to take advantage of the increased price of iron by developing mines on Exmoor. He was already at work at Blackland mine near Withypool, and in 1909 was granted a licence to search for ore on Exmoor until March 1911 on condition that £2000 was spent on the search. With his licence Roberts acquired a stack of 400 tons of ore left at Bluegate by Schneider and Hannay, which he sold to various buyers. In 1910 Roberts persuaded other ironmasters from the Midlands to join him and form the Exmoor Mining Syndicate. In 1911, the licence which had been assigned to the syndicate, was extended for a year, and exploratory work was carried out in the same areas as their predecessors in the 1850s, Deer Park, Picked Stones and Burcombe, but with as little success. In 1912 two members of the syndicate withdrew, leaving Roberts and Edward Prosser Davis of Bennerly Furnaces, Ilkeston, to carry on alone. They invited Lord Fortescue to join them to form the Exmoor Mining Syndicate Ltd which was registered in December 1912 with capital of £10,000.

The new syndicate worked adits in Burcombe and Picked Stones, and attempted to keep the shaft at Blue Gate unwatered, but as 1912 was one of the wettest years ever recorded, this attempt was largely unsuccessful. A shaft was sunk into the openworks at Burcombe and disused adits reopened, and a track from there to the South Molton road was surfaced to allow traction engines to haul ore from the mine to South Molton station. Small amounts of ore were taken from Burcombe and Blue Gate, but were sold for less than cost, and in

1913 these two mines were closed. Work was concentrated at Picked Stones, where in 1913 a tramway was laid from the mine up the hill to Gypsy Lane at SS 804386. About 30 tons of ore a week was being brought out, and transported to Dulverton station. In July 1914 the firms taking ore to the station resigned as they were making no profit and, being unable to replace them, the syndicate ceased operations. During the next two years, the partners tried to form a new company, but without success, and then to sell the mining property, but with equal lack of success, and finally in 1918 the syndicate was wound up.

Today there are few traces of the considerable efforts made to mine iron ore on Exmoor. The shafts are filled, and with few exceptions, the adits blocked. Reclamation for agriculture has effaced most of the remains at Picked Stones, so that only a collapsed adit about 88yd (80m.) long is visible. The openwork trench centred on SS 753381 is the most impressive remain on the moor, although the Main Drift at Cornham Ford is partly open at SS 750387. To the north of the Barle at Cornham Ford, and at Wheal Eliza, the remains of six miners' cottages may still be seen; also at Wheal Eliza the shaft is still open, although full of water, and there is a helpful interpretation board at this site.

Peripheral Iron Ore Mining Sites

Areas surrounding Exmoor and the Brendon Hills will be described beginning at Combe Martin and proceeding in a clockwise direction.

Combe Martin

Although best known for its silver-lead mines, Combe Martin parish also pro- duced iron ore. The first recorded working began in the last years of the eigh- teenth century near Wild Pear beach (SS 5847). In 1796 while visiting the area Swete recorded that he had a good view of the mine then being opened up there below Little Hangman. In that year George Fox of Perran Wharf in Cornwall had leased iron ore below the Combe Martin manorial land on Girt and Holdstone Downs (SS 6047 and 6147). It is not known if Fox was connected with the Wild Pear beach mine. Between 1796 and 1802 more than 9000 tons of ore were sent from here to Alexander Raby's ironworks at Llanelli.

The short-lived revival in North Devon iron mining in the 1850s and 1860s, largely initiated by Blackwell and Rogers, brought fresh activity to Combe Martin. Combe Martin New, or North Devon Iron Mine, as the enterprise was variously known, sent nearly 1600 tons of ore to South Wales in 1855-6, and, as demand for the non-phosphoric ores grew after the introduction of the Bessemer process, other ventures followed each other in rapid succession: The Hangman Hill Mining Co. in 1867, West of England Iron Ore Co. Ltd from 1868 to 1870, the Girt and Holdstone Downs Mining Co. Ltd in 1875-6, and the Comb-martin Manganese and Haematite Co. Ltd in 1877. The amounts of ore produced by these companies were insignificant and little remains on the ground to show where they worked.

Luccombe

At SS 913445 a small opencast mine was opened on top of Knowle Hill in the 1820s, but it is said the partners in the venture disagreed and abandoned it. Haematite was the mineral extracted, but to judge from the evidence on the ground, very little was taken out. The mine was at work again in 1836[4] and was reopened in 1872 by Carter and Barren of Plymouth for a short time, but the unexpired portion of their lease was advertised in the *Mining Journal* in 1880,[5] since when nothing more has been done at this site.

Wootton Courtenay

At SS 928428, near Brockwell, about a half a mile south west of Wootton Courtenay, are extensive remains of an opencast haematite mine. The first reference to it is in a geologist's report by Thomas Webster dated 1828[6] to Charles Bailey, Lord Sherborne's agent, in which he gave account of trial pits dug into the ore there. Following receipt of the report, Lord Sherborne began opencast workings on the site, selling the ore to Richard Crawshay of Cyfarthfa. Henry de la Beche mentioned the mine in 1839, when the captain was B. A. Ancell of Porlock,[7] but by 1848 Smith Tibbits, who had driven the level at Gupworthy on the Brendons, had leased the mine. The mine seems to have been worked out soon after and has been abandoned ever since.

Alcombe Mine

In 1870, Richard Gregory, who was prospecting in the area after the failure of his mine at Exford, is said to have found a lode of iron on Alcombe Common in the area SS 974446. In spite of much local celebration, and a visit from L. Vickery of Bere Alston who was interested in leasing the sett, the venture came to nothing. There is a local tradition of an adit into Knowle Hill at SS 967440, but this may be the remains of a much older copper mine.

Luckyard Mine

In 1873 William Gold of Luckyard farm, Exton leased to Morgan Morgans, the former mines captain of the Brendon Hills mines, certain fields of the farm with the right to dig for minerals there.[8] Twelve months later Morgans transferred the lease to William Gibbs, an ironmaster of Wombourne House, Wolverhampton. Gibbs seems to have been acting on behalf of the Exford Iron

Co., which was registered in January 1875 to buy all the interests of the partners in Luckyard mine. Two adits seem to have been driven, one in an easterly direction the other towards the south, close to South Quarme farm in the area of SS 924360. Remains of dumps are still visible, but apparently the mine did not pay its way, and closed in 1879-80.

Blackland Mine, Withypool

In the valley of Pennycombe Water at SS 841369 adits were driven east and west into the hillside by the Exford Iron Co., who were attracted to the site by the openworks on the hillside above. The Exford Iron Co. Ltd was registered on 4 January 1875[9] with four principal directors: Boaz Bloomer of Pelsall, Staffs, Richard Cripps of Bristol, who acted as mine captain, William Gibbs, an ironmaster of Wombourne House, Wolverhampton, and Frederick Perry of Dunstan, Staffs. By May 1875, 2300 £10 shares in the firm had been taken , and much of this money was expended in driving the levels and sinking a shaft on to the west adit about 250yd (225m.) from the portal. In April 1876 another 2000 shares were issued and work continued on the west adit, the eastern adit having been abandoned.

Because of its inaccessible position the directors decided to construct a 2ft (60cm.) gauge railway from Marsh Bridge near Dulverton following the course of the River Barle for a little over 9 miles up to the mine. The engineer was John Miles of Dulverton, and the plan was submitted for parliamentary approval at the end of November 1877. There is a note in the House of Lords Journals for 1878 to the effect that Standing Orders had been complied with, but nothing further was heard of the proposal. Unfortunately the presence of sulphides in the Blackland ore rendered the deposit valueless unless it was first calcined, but because of the heavy cost of bringing coal to the site this was not possible. Accordingly in 1881 the decision was taken to wind up the company. Plant was advertised for sale in December 1881 and again in June 1882, and the winding up was completed in June 1883. In March 1907 the Withypool Mining Co. was formed and began to send loads of ore from the stockpile by traction engine to Minehead. In the following year the Somerset Mineral Syndicate seems to have taken over their assets; they built an incline about 437yd (400m.) long from Pennycombe Water up to the Withypool road and by this means began to remove ore from the stockpile. Some of their plant at the mine was included in the Syndicate's sale in 1910. In March 1918 when iron prices rose, this mine was one of those taken over by the South Western Mining Syndicate Ltd, but apart from removing some ore left at the site, little was done, and the syndicate became moribund, being formally dissolved by the Registrar of Companies in 1927.

It is said that in 1937-8 the mine was cleared out, possibly by J. H. Bennetts who had been the principal mining engineer to the Somerset Mineral Syndicate. In 1941 the Home Ore Department believed that this was one of two sites on Exmoor (the other was Florence mine), that justified a detailed examination. Early in 1942 a troop of Canadian Royal Engineers were sent to the mine to carry out the necessary investigative work. They found that the shaft bottom was blocked by a fall, which the sappers cleared and inserted new supporting timbers in the adits which had been driven north east and south west from the shaft bottom. Within 115yd (105m.) from shaft bottom, the lode was displaced at both ends by faults, and the ore showed considerable contamination with copper, such that it was unsuitable for steel making. The Canadian R.E. left the site, since when no further work has been carried out at this mine.

Mines near Exford

In his *History of Neath Abbey* (1902) Walter de Grey Birch records a quotation from the 'Perambulations of five Forests of Somerset' of 1298 which stated that not far from Exford church 'are some very ancient ironworks, probably held from the Abbot of a monastery, in the furnaces of which the entire wood of the forest has been consumed'. It is most unlikely that Exmoor was ever in historic times a forest in the sense of a tree-clad area, so this evidence should not be relied upon. In 1550 Edward VI granted Michael Wynston a licence to work mines of 'iron and steel ore on Exmoor and Dartmoor, and there is a tradition, upheld by Collinson writing in 1791, that the site of this medieval mine was 1 1/2 miles east of Exford church, possibly in the area of Staddon Hill, SS 8837.

Recent authors have confused the geographical location with the Exford Iron Co. Ltd referred to above, but there is little doubt that Collins in 1912 and Cantrill in 1917 intended to refer to the firm rather than the village. There was however a mine near Exford known as Wheal Gregory about half a mile south of the village. A twenty-one year lease dated January 1857 was granted to Richard Gregory who at about this time issued a prospectus for the Wheal Gregory Iron and Copper Mine[10] with a capital of £5120 in £5 shares. In 1858 the land on which the mine stood was sold and the new owner commissioned a report on the mineral prospects from a Cornish mining engineer, who could find only iron there, and no copper. In 1860, the company seems to have been reformed as The Exford Mine and Colour Co. with offices in London. In a report of 1860 Joseph Henderson, a civil and mining engineer from Aberdare said that he was satisfied that at least 100 tons of ore a day could be sold at a profit of 5/- to 7/- (25p. to 35p.). Four adits seem to have been driven by Gregory and his partner Matthew Tresize; two in the area of SS 853376, west-wards into the hillside, and the others at SS 852374 east and west. All these adits are very short, so it is not surprising that the venture folded in 1863.

At SS 821376, about 875yd (800m.) south-west of the road junction at Sellbed

Cross, Dines records an adit with shaft about 87yd (80m.) to the south-west from which two lodes about 65yd (60m.) apart were worked. Nothing is known about who worked here or when.

Molland

About half a mile east of the village of Molland are the sites of two mines of great importance and considerable age, Bremley and Gourt. Here iron and copper ores were found in close association, and depending on the economic circumstances of the time, both have been extracted over many centuries. Recorded copper mining at these sites is covered elsewhere in this volume, but when the enormous upsurge in the demand for iron ores occurred in the third quarter of the nineteenth century the old Bremley mine (SS 818283) was re-opened by a consortium of Midlands ironmasters under the name of the Molland Iron and Manganese Mining Co. with the intention of working the iron lodes which lay immediately to the north of the previously worked copper lodes. In 1877 a Cornish mines captain, Henry Boyns, was appointed to oversee the reopening of the mine and a 37 ft (11.25m.) diameter waterwheel was pur-chased from Carnelloe mine at Zennor and installed in a new pit on the site of the old copper company's pumping wheel to drive pumps in the engine shaft. The installation started work in February 1878, and the mine was unwatered down to the 42 fathom (77m.) level by July.

The iron ore brought out was a mixture of haematite and spathic ore, but being contaminated with sulphides, required to be calcined before being offered for sale. It was burned in heaps with slack coal which drove off the sulphur dioxide and reduced the water content. This made the venture uneconomic, and in the following year the mine closed after selling only 387 tons of ore. In 1880 the mine was reopened but, as two members of the partnership were in financial difficulties, work was concentrated on selling ore already stockpiled. The Ebbw Vale Company complained about the uncalcined ore which was being sent to them, and in April 1880, they declined to buy any more. In that year 1681 tons of ore was raised by 12 men.

In 1882 Boyns left and was replaced as captain by Joseph Pope who had been captain at Bampfylde for many years. Underground working was resumed in 1882 and about 1500 tons a year was produced for the next six years. At Bremley, adits east and west of the engine shaft were linked by tramway to an ore hopper in the centre of the site at SS 818283. The east adit entered the hill-side at SS 818283 immediately to the west of the public road, and caused prob-lems in 1883 when the road began to subside into it. Although the Inspector of Mines required work to be carried out to remedy the situation, there is no evi-dence that anything was done. West of the engine shaft the lode was worked down to 20 fathoms (36.57m.) below the surface , but as the lode dipped to the south it seems to have been cut off by a nearly vertical copper lode. West of the stream an adit entered the hillside at SS 817283 and a shaft was sunk on to it a few yards to the west. About 50 yards to the north an adit was driven west into the hill and a tramway laid into it. Pope left in 1887 and John Brayley was appointed captain. Output increased to 4330 tons in 1891, but dwindled to nothing in 1893, and the mine closed in 1894. Today evidence of the former workings may still be seen. The site of the waterwheel pit and the leat can be identified as can the calcining bays and the adit entrances, but the whole area is much overgrown.

About 437yd (400m.) east of Bremley, at SS 823283, was Gourt mine. Like Bremley, this was originally a copper mine; indeed it is believed that the two workings were originally united underground. As a copper mine Gourt lasted longer than Bremley, closing in 1867. It was re-opened as an iron mine by the Molland Iron and Manganese Co. in 1877, and worked jointly with Bremley as one concern. Between them Bremley and Gourt produced about 28,000 tons of iron ore from 1877 to the end of 1892.

North Molton

An extensive group of workings was centred on Heasley Mill about one and a half miles north of North Molton. These are among the oldest mines in the area, indeed four ironworkers are recorded at North Molton in Domesday (1086).[11] In 1630 T. Westcote, in his *View of Devonshire* referred to the mining of iron at North Molton and Molland (Dixon, 1983, p. 60). There are numerous openworks in the area, indicative of very early mining activity, especially at Walscott (SS 7032), Barton (SS 7232) and Crowbarn Wood (SS 7331). There is evidence, too, of medieval smelting having been carried out at Stowford (SS 7131) and Bampfylde (SS 7332).

Historical iron mining in the area dates from the 1870s when the Carlist uprising in northern Spain caused a dire shortage of non-phosphoric ore in South Wales. Copper mines had by this date become unprofitable to work, but were re-opened as iron mines to meet the demand. In general the mines were worked for iron ore from 1873 to 1882 with a break in 1877-8 coinciding with the end of the Carlist uprising and the start of a prolonged depression in the iron and steel industry.

Bampfylde mine, which had been a very successful copper mine, was worked from 1873 onwards principally for iron ore, although both copper and small quantities of manganese were taken out as well. At this date James Mitchell was captain, but he left in 1874 and was replaced by James Julief from West Perranzabuloe. The company working the mine, the Bampfylde Mining Company, was called upon to repay a £600 loan to a bank which had gone into liquidation in 1877, but was unable to do so, and it went into liquidation also. In 1883 the North Molton Mining Co. took over the site, to be succeeded by the North Devon Mining Co. in 1885, but neither seems to have worked at Bampfylde, considering that the Stowford site seemed more promising. For a description of the workings and surface installations at Bampfylde see elsewhere in this volume.

Florence mine, SS 7532, was the most important and productive mine in the area. Massive deposits were found in wide lodes cut by a deep valley which could be worked by adits alone. The Florence Mining Co. was incorporated in December 1871 and appointed George Bush as captain. High quality haematite was taken out, but transport was, as usual, a major cost factor. The opening of the Devon and Somerset Railway from Taunton to Barnstaple in 1873 improved the situation, and the construction in 1874 of a tramroad from the mine to a siding on the railway a kilometre east of South Molton station gave Florence mine a considerable advantage over other mines in the area. The Bampfylde Co. started to build a branch to link with the main tramroad at SS 746311, but as the two companies were unable to agree on terms no connection was ever made.

In 1875 George Bush was replaced as captain by Dudley Bush. Between 1873 and 1878 a total of 20,693 tons of ore were produced with a value of £12,331, taken from three adits on the north side of the valley and two on the south side. The end of the Spanish Carlist uprising in 1876 caused a reduction in prices which resulted in the liquidation of the company in 1879. A slight improvement in the market in 1880 was reflected in the registration in that year of the New Florence mine which lasted until 1885, producing 17,693 tons of ore with a value of £14,267. The company did not go into liquidation until 1888, and was not formally wound up until 1892.

The rise in the price of iron during the First World War caused the reopening of several mines in the area. At Florence, the South Western Mining Syndicate was registered in April 1918 with plans to convert the former tramway into an aerial ropeway, but the accession to the title of a new Lord Poltimore, the ground landlord, who had an aversion to mining, made the project doubtful. A licence had already been granted to the company by his father, and it could not be stopped, but when the licence expired in 1920, Lord Poltimore declined to renew it, and in 1926 the syndicate was wound up.

Florence was the second mine to be reopened by the Home Ore Department in 1942 when investigations were being carried out into British haematite and manganese ores resources. An attempt was made to pump out a shaft inside one of the adits by a troop of Canadian Royal Engineers in the autumn of 1941, but their equipment was not equal to the task. In the following summer the shaft and adit at the bottom were pumped out, and the driving of the adit continued. Unfortunately the sappers broke into old workings which had not been shown on the abandonment plans, and the workings were flooded once more. Again they were pumped out and driving of the adit continued; but after less than 10 yards, the lode petered out and was replaced by a clay track, and it was decided not to proceed further with exploratory work.

Other mines in the area include Barton pits, referred to above, which were re-opened by the Bampfylde mine partnership in 1873, but no work was in fact carried out there. The old mine at SS 738318 in Crowbarn Wood was reworked in 1873 by the Bampfylde Co., but work here ceased in the following year. At SS 787300, just to the south of Twitchen, Pulsworthy mine was opened in 1873 by A. R. and J. Granger of Glasgow and during the next two years produced about 200 tons of ore, before closing. This working may also have been known as Marcia mine. In 1873 Granger Brothers reopened Walscott mine which had probably not been worked since the sixteenth century. A lode of spathic ore varying in width from 2-20 feet (60cm. to 6m.) was traced, but it soon dwindled to nothing and in 1875 further work was abandoned.

Stowford mine was at SS 713319 on the site of former openworks, and was re-opened in 1873 by the Bampfylde Mining Co. when they were prospecting for iron ore. They worked on two manganese lodes and three iron lodes from four shafts and two adits, one of which yielded between 12 and 15 tons of ore a fathom (1.8m.). After the company's liquidation Stowford was worked by the North Molton Mining Co. and their successors the North Devon Mining Company until they too closed in 1887. Altogether 2382 tons of ore were taken out of the mine.

Footnotes
1. *Victoria County History of Somerset* II (1911), 392-3.
2. GRO Npt 168 (M.350).
3. *Mining Journal*, 13 January 1855.
4. *Mining Journal*, 1836, p148.
5. *Mining Journal*, 1880, Vol 2, p.1093.
6. University College London MSS Misc 2W.
7. Somerset R.O. DD/WY box 143.
8. Devon R.O. Docs nos. 1044B addl. and 2/T 2/66.
9. PRO BT 31/2061.
10. I am grateful to J.K. Ridler (via M. Warburton) for this information.
11. *VCH Devon*, 1, 403 quoted in Dixon (1983).

Bibliography and Acknowledgements

Atkinson, M. and Baber, C., *The Growth and Decline of the South Wales Iron Industry, 1760-1880*, 1987.

Birch, A.,	*The Economic History of the British Iron and Steel Industry*, 1967.
Burton, R. A.,	*The Heritage of Exmoor*, 1989.
Claughton, P. F.,	'Molland: Iron Mining' (unpublished article).
	'Introduction: Iron Mining Nineteenth Century' (unpublished article), 1991.
Dines, H. G.,	*The Metalliferous Mining Region of South West England*, 1956.
Dixon, D.,	'Mining and the Community in the Parishes of North Molton, South Molton, Molland and Twitchen, Devonshire' (unpublished thesis, University of Southampton), 1983.
Flinn, M. W.,	'British steel and Spanish ore 1871-1914' in *Economic History Review*, 1955.
Gray-Jones, A.,	*A History of Ebbw Vale*, 1970.
Groves, A. W.	*Wartime Investigations into the Haematite and Manganese Ore Resources of Great Britain and Northern Ireland*, 1952.
John, A. H.,	*The Industrial Development of South Wales, 1750-1850*, 1950.
Jones, M. H.,	'Wartime Mining on Exmoor' in *Exmoor Review* Vol. 20, 1979, pp.41-5.
Marshall, J. D.,	*Furness and the Industrial Revolution*, 1958.
Percy, J.,	*Metallurgy: Iron and Steel*, 1864.
Savage, J.,	*A History of the Hundred of Carhampton*, 1830.
Schubert, H. R.,	*History of the British Iron and Steel Industry ... to 1775*, 1957.
Sellick, R. J.,	*The West Somerset Mineral Railway and the Story of the Brendon Hills Iron Mines*, 1962, 1970.
Tylecote, R. F.,	*A History of Metallurgy*, 1976.
VCH,	*Victoria County History of Somerset*, 1911.
Youell, R. F.,	*A Reassessment of Groves' Work on the Mineral Deposits of Exmoor: Report to the Institute of Geological Sciences*, 1974.

My particular thanks are due to Peter Claughton, David Dixon, Roger Burton and Mick Warburton for making freely available to me the fruits of their many years of work on the mines of North Devon and Exmoor, much of which has not yet been published.

COPPER AND GOLD MINING
IN THE EXMOOR AREA

David Dixon

(with a note on the Gourt Mine Engine House by Peter Claughton)

North Molton Gold

The existence of gold ore at North Molton is a well established fact but, before abandoning all to spend a life panning the gravels on the banks of the Mole, any would-be prospector would do well to examine historical precedents.

In 1797, the Revd Richard Polwhele in his *Devonshire* (p.69) recorded a Mr Chapple's observation that gold had been extracted from the copper mine. The current R.G.S. manual of gold sites correctly includes North Molton. The discovery was reliable and well authenticated. No less an authority than Sir Henry de la Beche stated in 1839 that gold 'has been discovered in grains and small plates among haematite iron ore, in a lode at the copper mine in North Molton'. The printed source he cites is Lysons' *Devonshire* (1822) which in turn states that gold had been '... found of late by Mr Flexman of South Molton in native grains in the copper mine at North Molton, occurring in a matrix of black and red oxide of iron'. Examination of the evidence on which this statement was based reveals the source to be a letter from the geologist William Wavell of Barnstaple (after whom Wavellite is named), dated 1 February 1822.[1] In this Wavell informed Daniel Lysons 'Gold was found by Mr Flexman, an eminent surgeon of South Molton – in the copper mine at North Molton – a fine specimen of which is now in his possession.' The only copper mine active in the parish of North Molton at this time was the Prince Regent Company's working at the Higher Mines Wood site. For almost thirty years, the discovery remained a matter of scientific note but of little commercial interest. It is clear, however, that the promoters of the Prince Albert mine in 1840 on a site lower down the river at Heasley Mill allowed for the possibility of gold being discovered.

In January 1848, far away in California, John A. Sutter discovered gold in the tail race of a water powered saw mill he was building. His discovery precipitated the 1849 California Gold Rush which notably triggered off the Australian Gold Rush of 1851. Consequently, dreams of gold were in the air in 1852 when the idea of a British gold mine was promoted with the enthusiastic support of the *Mining Journal*. Shares were advertised in the issue of 22 May 1852. The site of the new Britannia Gold and Copper mine was Higher Mines Wood, where Mr Flexman's discovery had been made.

Two months later Dr John Percy, author of the famous *Metallurgy* and a lecturer in the new Museum of Practical Geology, told a group of emigrants to the Australia gold fields that he did not believe gold to exist in economic quantities in England. In his characteristically forthright manner, he told his audience he did not care whom he offended and referred to 'glowing prospectuses' only 'calculated to mislead'. As the only company having issued a prospectus, the Britannia promoters were most offended.[2] A furious exchange in the *Mining Journal* led Percy to back off, but not down. Characteristically he was to be proved exactly right – gold was not present in economic quantities.

Meanwhile, down the valley at Heasley Mill, a second company, the Poltimore Copper and Gold Mining Company, reopened an old copper working. On the strength of its prospects a further company, the South Poltimore, was promoted. On 5 May 1853 the Poltimore shareholders meeting had a 26 oz. lump of gold on the table before them. The samples sent to Rawkins and Watson of St Helens for assay were very satisfactory.[3]

A year later, on 13 June 1854, a very different meeting was held. Further samples tested at St Helens and tests by Berdan machines on the mine had been equally discouraging. The sample taken to the Mersey, in a cutter aptly named the *Albatross,* had been 'salted'. This was simply the application of gold dust to the sample during the journey to ensure a favourable test result.

No-one was ever brought to book but the resulting scandal was enough not only to finish the Poltimore as a gold (but not as a copper) mine, but also to finish the Britannia and seriously damage far more respectable gold prospects in Wales.

One of the Britannia's and Poltimore's most ardent critics was a Cornishman, a quarry manager working at Wiveliscombe: 'I cannot refrain from noticing ... even shares in mines strongly recommended often go abegging, till some knaves get hold of the sell, and retain some 12,000 of the 20,000 free shares, when they rig the market, and off they send their shares.' He advised speculators '... to cast the golden fleece to the wind and stick with vigour to that baser metal, copper.'[4]

It is good advice and we shall now take it.

Copper Mining at North Molton

On 22 February 1346 (the year of the Battle of Crecy), Nicholas de Welliford attended the royal court at Westminster to be granted the keeping of the king's copper mine at North Molton. He was also granted wages and required to answer at the Exchequer. The following 13 November he was back, claiming that he had started operations, lost heavily and could see no profit in the work. His commission was duly surrendered and cancelled.[5] The recording of this failed working secured a place for North Molton on the relatively select list of medieval copper workings.[6]

North Molton and Molland parishes contain the significant copper sites of the Exmoor area. In the wider North Devon and West Somerset mineral district, significant amounts of copper have been raised in the Quantock Hills[7] and probably from Coddon Hill near Bishops Tawton.[8]

Within the parishes of North Molton and Molland, copper is known to have been mined in the Bampfylde mine at Heasley Mill, at Higher Mines Wood and, in Molland parish, Gourt and Bremley and near the Methodist Chapel.

Given subsequent history, it is almost certainly Heasley Mill that was the site of Nicholas de Welliford's working and also the mine reported to Henry VIII by Peter the German (Petrus Filius Almayn) as a copper mine at North Molton 'belonging to Mr Seymour'.[9]

Nicholas de Welliford's charter had referred to 'the king's copper mine at North Molton'; it may imply an earlier working or simply have reminded the reader that copper was a royal metal and that the king owned all mines discovered and undiscovered. In the sixteenth and seventeenth centuries, these rights were exercised with limited success by the Mines Royal and Mineral and Battery Works companies. In 1689, a very significant year in the history of English mineral extraction, the dead hand of monopoly was removed and mining endeavour blossomed in many places, including North Molton.

Any newly arrived inhabitants who required the services of the church and entry in the North Molton parish registers before they had stayed long enough to be considered fully resident in North Molton had their parishes of origin entered. Between 1698 and 1704, and 1714 and 1733, many Cornish names appear. They represent only the tip of an iceberg since doubtless the majority of newly arrived miners did not require marriage, baptism or funeral. Of a total of 32 names appearing in both periods, 14 appear in 1699 alone. The figures as a whole represent a steady flow with a major influx in 1699.[10] The human element in this is best preserved in the instance of Ralph Mitchell who moved to North Molton with his wife and child in 1721 and was granted a certificate stating that in the event of hardship the family would remain the responsibility of the overseers of the poor in Gwinear.[11]

The substantial results of the labour of miners such as Ralph Mitchell are preserved in the Barnstaple Port books.[12] The figures appear in six-monthly folios predating the 1751 adoption of the Gregorian Calendar with New Year's Day on 25 March. Copper ore exports appear regularly from 1696 onwards until 1720, after which the books are either unavailable or lost. Major quantities of ore were exported between 1697 and 1702, reaching a peak in April-September 1699 when well over 400 tons were exported. From 1706 to 1714 exports remained at less than 50 tons a year. After this they began to increase but remained below 150 tons until October-March 1720 when the amount increased to 250 tons. Earlier destinations centred on Bristol and Chepstow but included Neath and London. Later ores were exclusively sent to Bristol, but after this the figures are unavailable. The figures need to be treated with some caution since there were potential additional sources at Molland and possibly Codden Hill. Undoubtedly the North Molton mine was the major source.

In 1698 and 1725 the North Molton mine was visited by two Swedish mining officials, Thomas Cletscher and Henrik Kahlmeter, each leaving a detailed description of the mine.[13] It is in the contrast between their descriptions that we can best see developments at the mine.

'From here (Minehead) I went to North Molton in Devonshire where the rich copper mines are which were dug four years ago ...' wrote Thomas Cletscher. The site was owned by a widow who leased the mine to 'some private partici-pants'. The mine was clearly at a pioneering stage. The workmen were 'so unaccustomed to mining that they leave off the mine as soon as the vein is lost without further searching for it'. The ore was to be raised by a hand gin in small baskets but this was not yet in service. The shafts were narrow and lined with wood, the deepest was not below 35 fathoms (64m.). The workforce was about 150 men who were paid 7/6d. (37 p.) per week. This was a good rate and was attracting miners from Cornwall. Three lodes, running north east and south west, were being worked. The poor ore was selling for £6-7 on the mine while the best reached £8-10-0. This compared favourably with £3-4 per ton that a contemporary mine near Truro was able to get. The ore was carried by pack horse to Barnstaple at a cost of 2/10d. Apart from the South Wales colliers, vessels were unable to cross the Barnstaple bar and the ore was shipped out in the local flat bottomed barges.

In 1725 Henrik Kahlmeter described the mine as split 'in two works, which are run on both sides of the little River Moule'. The size of the dumps were suf-ficient in his eyes to confirm its reputation as the oldest mine in England. The ore had been 'found in larger quantities than nowadays, so that where they had got 30, 40 or 45 tons a month, they are now not able to go beyond 20, ... Correspondingly the workforce had reduced to eighty,' ... both mine servants and stampers, of whom the former receive 30/- (£1.50) a month, a similar rate to Cletscher's day.

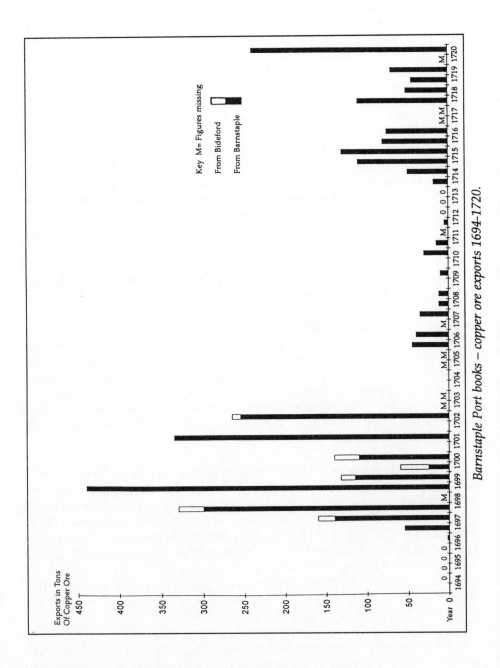

Barnstaple Port books – copper ore exports 1694-1720.

The management of the mine was vastly different, being run by the 'Bristol Company'. This was less a company and more a combination of Bristol copper smelters. William Pryce, recalling them in 1778, defined them as 'The four copper Companies, viz the Brass-Wire Company, the English Copper Company, Wayn and Chambers and Company, being then united and confederated, there can be no doubt of their beholding with a single eye their joint interest and pursuit'.[14] It is no surprise to learn that the ore was not sold by the proprietors and bought the ground owners part 'at the cheap price of 3 pounds sterling per ton'. The best ore was said to yield 1 ton of copper from 2 tons of ore.

Pryce describes the south western mining interest as having been 'subject to the dominations of rapacious and dishonest combinations' but it is clear that the smelters' stranglehold ensured that the mine at North Molton at least was well run. The most spectacular evidence for this were the twin water engines that Kahlmeter describes as draining the eastern and western sections. They were of a type similar to those shown on Pryce's sectional plate showing Ballen Garden mine.

The burial of Francis Case on 15 August 1733 marked the last new arrival from Cornwall for thirty years and it is clear that shortly after his death the mine ceased operations. It was reopened in or about 1760, a working that lasted for about twelve years or a little longer before, like many Cornish mines, it was rendered uneconomic by the flood of cheap copper ore that emanated from the Parys Mountain mines on Anglesey. By far the most valuable survival from this period was the section drawn by John Blake, schoolmaster from Bishop's Nympton. It records the North Woods Copper mine – as it was then called – almost at the end of its eighteenth century phase. Blake produced two draft drawings and a key in a letter for a prospective plate and they are shown here as recorded by Dixon in 1983.[15]

The mine is shown as two sections on either side of the valley. There was only one communication drift below ground. The eastern workings are shown completely, the western section of the mine was only partially open and was clearly more extensive. The eastern engine shaft was operative but the western (K) is shown as 'The Old Engine Shaft'. The Deep Bottoms in the eastern section were pumped by a chain and churn pump. Thirteen shafts are shown and in 1983 it was possible to trace them eastward from the site of the South House Shaft (p) either as reworked Victorian shafts or as depressions in the ground. The deepest section of the mine was the Deep Adit linked to the eastern engine shaft 45 fathoms (83m.) below the eastern top adit level.

Apart from being a testimony to the surveying talents of John Blake, the section is ample testimony to the extent of the early-eighteenth century operations. It is certainly comparable with the section of Pool mine (near Camborne)

46

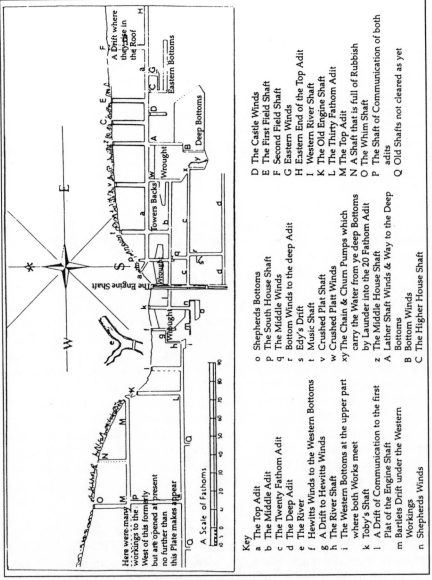

West Wood copper mine, North Molton. Based upon the sections drawn by John Blake in 1772. John Blake's original terms have been retained, but the spelling has been updated for the sake of clarity.

A Scale of Fathoms.

Here were many workings to the West of this formerly but are opened at present no further than this Plate makes appear

Key

a The Top Adit
b The Middle Adit
c The Twenty Fathom Adit
d The Deep Adit
e The River
f Hewitts Winds to the Western Bottoms
g A Drift to Hewitts Winds
h The River Shaft
i The Western Bottoms at the upper part where both Works meet
k Toby's Shaft
l A Drift of Communication to the first Plat of the Engine Shaft
m Bartlets Drift under the Western Workings
n Shepherds Winds

o Shepherds Bottoms
p The South House Shaft
q The Middle Winds
r Bottom Winds to the deep Adit
s Edy's Drift
t Music Shaft
v Crushed Plat Shaft
w Crushed Platt Winds
xy The Chain & Churn Pumps which carry the Water from ye deep Bottoms by Launder into the 20 Fathom Adit
z The Middle House Shaft
A Lather Shaft Winds & Way to the Deep Bottoms
B Bottom Winds
C The Higher House Shaft

D The Castle Winds
E The First Field Shaft
F Second Field Shaft
G Eastern Winds
H Eastern End of the Top Adit
I Western River Shaft
K The Old Engine Shaft
L The Thirty Fathom Adit
M The Top Adit
N A Shaft that is full of Rubbish
O The Whim Shaft
P The Shaft of Communication of both adits
Q Old Shafts not cleared as yet

A Drift where they rise in the Roof
Eastern Bottoms
Deep Bottoms
Towers Backs
Wrought
The Engine Shaft

published by William Borlase in 1758 in his *Natural History of Cornwall*. It was clearly not on the scale of the Bullen Garden mine as shown by Pryce in *Mineralogia Cornubiensis* but, assuming that development work in the 1760s working was limited, the majority of the North Woods mine was already fifty years old.

On 20 March 1802 the vicar of North Molton conducted the funeral of Captain George Rowe, described in the burial register as fifty-six years old and 'captain of the mines'. He had been involved in the reopening of the mine. This reworking was that mentioned by Charles Vancouver in his *General View of the Agriculture of Devon* published in 1808. In 1815 John Taylor (the famous mining entrepreneur who worked Wheal Friendship at Mary Tavy) told Daniel Lysons that the old mine had since been given up.[16] Little is known in detail about the working but the famous engineer John Rennie was asked to design a waterwheel to pump the mine. His specification was addressed to 'Messrs Ward Rohde and Co.'

It is almost certainly this working that features in an unattributed early-nineteenth century painting at Court Hall, North Molton. This shows the mine from the north. Dumps are clear on the western hill and on the valley floor. An indentation on the eastern hill almost certainly marks the leat. On the dumps in the centre, three men work near a simple triangular headgear.

In his note to Lysons, John Taylor had referred 'the old mine since given up'. The word 'old' is significant because there was also a new mine. This was at Higher Mines Wood. On 20 December 1809 John Williams of Scorrior obtained a licence from Sir Charles Warwick Bampfylde which referred to the '... load now opened and cut by the said John Williams, his partners and co-adventurers'.[17] These trials were transferred the following year into the Prince Regent mine, named in honour of the elevation of George, Prince of Wales, to Regent in 1810. Little is known of the detail of this working but the parish registers testify to the continuation of mining activity until at least 1840 and the company may have survived until as late as 1849. The prospectus for a fresh venture in 1852 refers to 'All the necessary machinery for mining purposes' being on the property, to which the modern appliances would be added.[18] It was at this mine that the 1822 particles of gold were found.

In 1840 the Heasley Mill mine was reopened as the Prince Albert, named after Queen Victoria's new consort. There were monetary difficulties for the principal proprietor and the mine was under-invested. The mining materials were sold by auction in April 1845. For the first time since 1802 there were no copper miners working at North Molton.

The revival of both sites as gold mines has been considered above. After the disreputable episode in 1854, the Poltimore mine, on the Heasley Mill site, survived uncertainly as a copper mine until 1856 when it was replaced by the Bampfylde Mining Company. It is this name that has stayed with the site. The new company had offices in Liverpool, the secretary and purser being Charles Hand of that city, and its local agent was Captain James Pope. He was born at Breage in Cornwall and was to remain active in North Devon mining for the rest of the century, remaining as captain at the Bampfylde until 1870. During his reign the mine was well managed but never really prospered. Mrs Bawden of Heasley Mill told E. R. Delderfield in the 1950s that she remembered Captain Pope as a splendid type of man, superintendent of the Sunday School and living in a fine house in the middle of the workings. He last appears in *White's Directory of 1900* as 'Joseph Pope, Mining Engineer of 7 Orchard Terrace, Barnstaple'.

In 1862 *Williams' Mining Directory* describes the mine as 80 fathoms deep and as employing 40 people who were paid on the second Saturday of each month. Chowen discussing Devon mining in 1863 describes the Bampfylde mine as producing 'copper ores in quantities sufficient to defray working expenses ...'. Captain Pope, true to instinct as a Cornishman, was sinking a large shaft into the western hill. He would have remembered the experience of Dolcoath mine which had twice saved itself by discovering fresh lodes beneath its existing workings. The Bampfylde No. 4 Shaft is Joseph Pope's inverted monument reaching into the earth. In 1856 *Kelly's Directory* could report then it was 20 fathoms (37m.); by 1862 it had reached 102 fathoms (186m.) below adit – 612 feet below adit and 852 feet (260m.) below surface, and ultimately it reached 157 fathoms (287m.) below surface (Dines 1956).

Apart from No. 4 Shaft, a lode to the north was explored from Hands Shaft – named after Charles Hand. The eastern workings were also reworked and several shafts enlarged.

Such development was clearly a drain on resources. A new fifteen-year lease was obtained from Lord Poltimore and on 4 March 1854 the mine was auctioned as a going concern, the purchaser being James Ockeston of Liverpool. The New Bampfylde Copper Mining Company Ltd was again Liverpool based and employed James Pope as Captain and Charles Hand as secretary. Like many mining companies, it took advantage of the Companies Act of 1860 which gave limited liability to joint stock companies. Liability under the former cost-book system had been unlimited. By 1868, the local workforce had increased to 61 men, four women and 15 boys. A further ten men were employed on tribute – independent sub-contractors who bid against each other to work given areas underground.

Finance was still a problem and in 1868 Charles Hand, now chairman, reported that shareholders 'could not without serious inconvenience con-

49

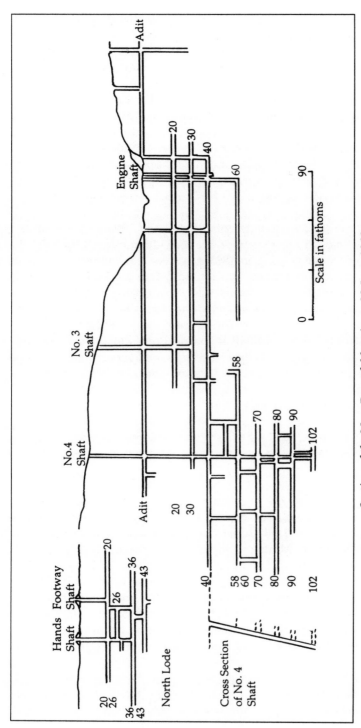

Section of the New Bampfylde mine – 23 June 1868.
Based upon a sale inventory. Fathom levels given as follows: 40.

tribute' and that the company's assets would be sold. Although a prospectus, including full plans and an inventory were produced[19] the sale never took place as Lord Poltimore made further concessions to save the company. The 1868 inventory does not include the Jigging Machine and Picking Table invented by Captain Pope and known to have been installed by 1870.[20] This was yet another symptom of an attempt to cut costs and exploit lower grades of ore. Despite everything the company succumbed in or about 1870. The mine was sold and Captain Pope left.

The Bampfylde Copper Mining Company Limited was yet another Liverpool based company. Maudsley and Co.'s *Monthly Reflex upon Mines and Mining* in 1873 reported of the Bampfylde 'This valuable property is progressing satisfactorily, and from yield of metallic ores both copper and iron the company cannot fail ere long to reward shareholders.'

However copper mining was in terminal decline. The peak years of production in the South West had been 1855-6. Between 1865 and 1870, production was reduced by half, and by 1874 only three major copper mines survived. Maudsley and Co.'s report mentioned the high quality of the copper ore which is consistent with earlier experience. It was thus the market that snuffed out the copper production at the Bampfylde, although it is likely that it would never have regained its glory days of the eighteenth century, even with the areas that No. 4 Shaft made accessible.

The company was saved, for a while at least, by the demand for spathic iron ore occasioned by the Spanish civil war of the 1870s. The company went into liquidation in 1879.

A photograph taken in about 1870 and reproduced in Walter Minchinton's *Devon at Work* (1974) captures the mine at the end of its copper career. It is clearly posed, with management well to the fore. It is tempting to imagine Captain Pope and Charles Hand among them but in reality it could equally show the last Bampfylde company upon accession. The picture is taken from the vantage point of the crusher house and looks north across the dressing floors and their sheds. The stands carrying the winding rope powered by the crusher wheel lead towards the Engine Shaft, the headgear of which dominates the scene. To the right is the upper portion of the waterwheel that powered the pumps. Behind this are the chimneys of the captain's house and exactly level with the ridge of its roof is a faint horizontal line. This is the launder that crossed the valley taking water from the leat and away to the right to a pond in the trees below the almost indiscernible building on the western hill. From here the water travelled along a leat to feed a further waterwheel behind the prominent white L-shaped building on the left. The purpose of this building is unknown but it may have contained the offices. The River Mole runs between

51

this building and the dumps in front of it. In front of the dressing sheds, to the left, a miner sits on a waggon. Above him in the dark shadows of the western hills the dim outline of a structure leading up the hill can be seen. These were 172 fathoms (315m.) of rods indicated in the 1868 inventory which led from the Engine Wheel in the valley to No. 4 Shaft to power the pumps deep in the western hill. The water was pumped to adit level rather than the surface.

The North Molton Copper Site Remains

The following site descriptions are based upon observations gathered between 1976 and 1983.[21]

The Bampfylde Mine Site – (SS 739328)

This description relates to the plan of the site (opposite). The workings lie east-west across the steep sided Mole valley about one third of a mile north of Heasley Mill. The country rock is Devonian shale. The minerals were worked along three lodes on the west of the valley: the North Lode, the main Poltimore Lode and the South or Bampfylde Lode. The eastern workings exploited an eastern extension of the Poltimore Lode. The line of shafts on the eastern side of the valley are early eighteenth century in origin. In all, the site had no less than 21 shafts. Fourteen of these are recorded on Blake's section of 1772. Apart from the Engine Shaft, those on the eastern side of the valley were found to be traceable either as depressions or, in two cases, as reworked Victorian shafts. Nineteenth century working, dominated by No. 4 Shaft, overwhelm almost all earlier evidence on the western hill. No. 3 Shaft on the brow of the hill was filled. The site of Hands Shaft on the North Lode was marked by spoil heaps east of the bank between two fields north west of No. 4 Shaft and described, on the 1842 Tithe Map, as 'Mines Field' and 'Western Mines Field'.

The workings were served by the large leat still clearly visible on the eastern hill. It drew from the River Mole to the north east of the mine and follows the contour of the eastern hill to a point south of the workings and above the crusher house. Below this it is discharged into a channel leading back to the river. North of the mine workings it was 3ft (0.9m.) deep and 8ft (2.4m.) wide; this width reduces to 6ft (1.8m.) south of the workings. It served the crusher house wheel, the dressing floors, the engine shaft wheel and the launder crossing the valley. There was no indication of a pit for the engine shaft wheel.

On the western side of the valley, at an approximately similar level to the eastern leat, was a large narrow pound following the contour of the hill which opened onto a leat leading southward across the line of the dumps and arrived above a wheel pit lying east west. The east wall was dismantled but the

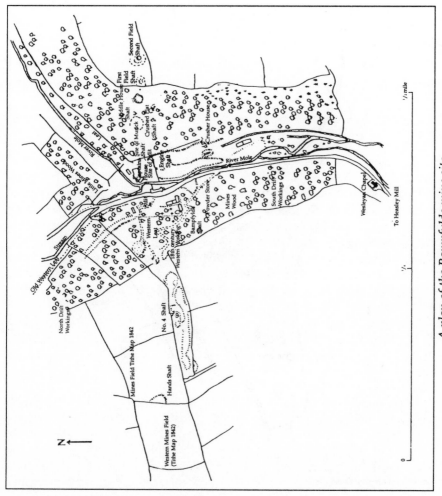

A plan of the Bampfylde mine site.
Based upon the Ordnance Survey 25in. Plan surveyed in 1888.

Second Field Shaft

First Field Shaft

Middle House

Site of Mudck

Crushed Bat

Shaft

Crusher House

Lane

River Mole

Engine Shaft

Site of Old House

Site of Adit

River Mole

Crusher House

Powder Store

Mine Wood

South Drift Workings

Bampfylde Shaft

Wesleyan Chapel

To Heasley Mill

Western Adit

Western Leat

18th century Western Workings

North Drift Workings

"Old Western Leat"

Stream

Mines Field Tithe Map 1842

No. 4 Shaft

Hands Shaft

Western Mines Field (Tithe Map 1842)

N

0

½

½ mile

respond for an exit arch remained. The pit measured 54ft (16.4m) by 8ft (2.4m), and was almost certainly the site of a 50ft (15.2m) waterwheel described as being 'taken down' at the time of the 1868 inventory.

A leat was identified running near the base of the western hill. It must have been fed by the tributary of the Mole that joins the river above the mine site. Its

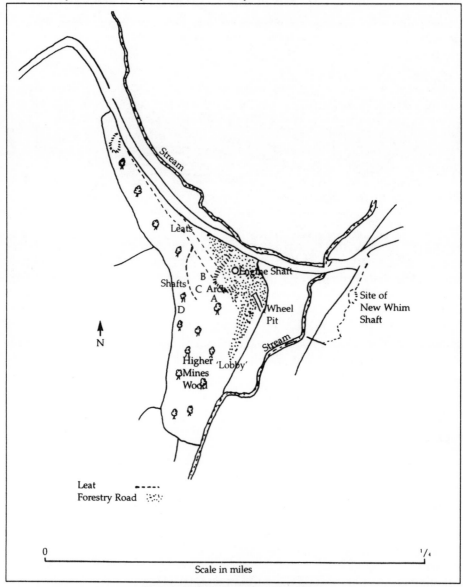

Higher Mines Wood, North Molton.
Based upon the Ordnance Survey 25in. Plan of 1888.

path was much disturbed and it is possible that this was the leat that fed one of the engines Kahlmeter observed in 1725.

The most interesting building on the site, the crusher house (SS 732326), was powered by a 30ft (9.1m.) waterwheel, which had an attached drawing whim. Its pit is clearly visible next to the crusher house. This was a two storey building and its function is described below under 'dressing'. A further possible crushing area has recently been identified by quantities of ore found on the western side of the river below the mine. It is perhaps too much to hope that this is the site of Captain Pope's jigging machine!

Next to No. 4 Shaft are the clear footings for a steam engine with the ruins of a stone boiler house next to it. This is the site of the horizontal steam engine mentioned in the inventory of 1868, which was housed in a wooden shed.

Of the other buildings on the mine, including the captain's house, smithy and workshops, only very limited evidence remained above ground.

The Higher Mines Wood Site – (SS 746335)

This was the site of the 1820's gold find. Its site was much obscured by the arrival of a forestry road driven across the site during the period of survey. This covered the large depression which marked the site of the former engine shaft and the remains of the pit for a 50ft (15.2m.) waterwheel. Only the exit arch is visible at the foot of the steep embankment that carries the new road. A small stream, possibly from the workings, issued from it and along a straight cut leading to the river, and is known to have been built by the gold mining company. In the plantation above the road the depressions for four shafts (A to D on plan) and two leats were visible. From these, the engine shaft and a shaft site of the New Whim Shaft on the eastern side of the river, it seems likely that the workings lay east west across the site.

Copper Mining at Molland

The four copper mining sites at Molland are centred upon a lode of iron and copper east of Molland village. They are found near Molland Methodist chapel, at Ford and Bremley, Danes Pits at Gourt Cross and in the valley south of Gourt Farm.

The first mining at Molland was for iron and the first reference to it made by Westcote's Devon in the seventeenth century.[22] There is evidence of open work although the name Danes Pits suggests an eighteenth-century attribution for an old working, possibly a shaft.

By a lease dated 20 October 1719 John Courtenay granted the mining rights at Ford tenement, near Bremley Farm to Robert Challacombe, described as a tinner from Combe Martin.[23] When Henrik Kahlmeter reported on the site in 1725 he noted 'where several old shafts were sunk down, the deepest of which was of 14 fathoms (26m.). The small amount of [copper] ore, which is there now is intermingled with a strong iron binding.' He also noted shafts at Danes Pits.[24]

In the mid eighteenth century Dean Jeremiah Milles of Exeter, contemplating writing a history of Devon, requested all the clergy between 1747 and 1756 to obtain a variety of information, including mining, on their respective parishes. The vicar of Molland, John Coleridge, engaged an unnamed local source 'a gentleman who has seen the loads'[25] to provide a written statement. Of an unworked shaft at Ford he noted a lode or vein of copper near the surface for 6 fathoms and for 6 or 7 fathoms (11-13m.) deep, well spotted and tinctured with copper and near 3ft (1m.) wide. Of Danes Pits, he tells us that they had been 'wrought no less than three several times in this century and a great many tuns of copper ore have been sent off from here by the undertakers'.

Both Henrik Kahlmeter and the Dean Milles material mention a working on the tenement of Copphall. Writing in or after 1747 the Dean's informant described the first working: 'Cophole works were discovered about thirty years since and the first days work by one man and who was the first or at least on of the first that discovered it gote a Tun of good Copper Oar.' In 1725 Kahlmeter described a derelict working 'The first was worked not long ago by Neash from Bristol but now laid waste. This lode seemed to be the same or at least of the same nature with the following, which is called Ford ...'.

An amplification of Henry Nashe's working and details of a further workings are given by Dean Milles' informant.

> But the best work of all is supposed to be at Cophole and which is of a very late discovery. The ore being more Ritcher than any of the former. The Gentlemen that undertook this work being advised to sink a shaft and erect an engine which cost upwards of £500 by reason of which and finding no profitt came in ordered the works to be stopt without any further Tryal or rather without any tryall at all by this last company which were Bristol gentlemen. But Henry Nash Esq and Co. who were the first that adventured in this work gote vast quantities of very good copper ore and, had they had Justice done 'em by their agents and work men believe would have gote considerable by it. The Engine Shaft was sunk 24 fathoms (44m.) deep but of no use as there was none made of it.

The writer clearly reflects local opinion, confirmed by the vicar's covering note for Dean Milles, 'This is what I can yet collect of Molland there was formerly a mine of copper where some Calamine was likewise found; but by the

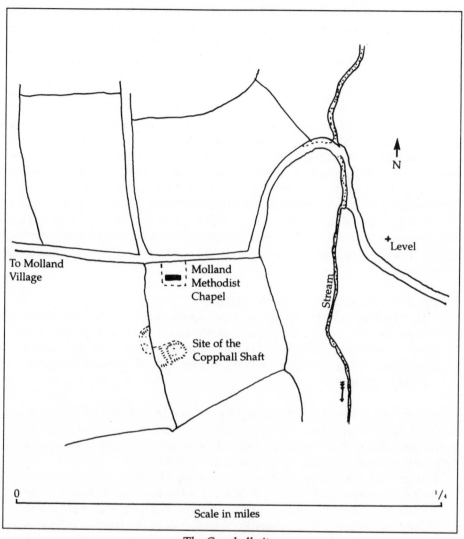

The Copphall site.
Based upon the Ordnance Survey 25in. Plan of 1889.

knowing of workmen the work desisted; tho all agree that the mine was very valuable.'

The key to all this lies in the identity of 'the Bristol gentlemen'. On 20 July 1734 William and Mary Paston (the inheritors of the Courtenay estates in Molland) granted mining rights to Thomas Castor (Coster) of Bristol on certain tenements. Rights to mine were conferred at Copphall and Addlehole, those on North Stone, Creeches and South Stone were extended.[26] This lease clearly separates this working from those at Ford and Bremley and is a direct reference to

57

the famous Coster family who did so much to open up West Country mining early in the eighteenth century. Thomas Coster, M.P. for Bristol, died in 1739, the only one in his generation to leave an heir, a daughter. After this the family business contracted and events at Copphall mine were no doubt part of this.

The site of the mine is harder to determine than the other sites. By the time of the Tithe Map in 1843, Copphall had been incorporated with Rosehays and parts of Mousehole and Addlehole. The only shaft site in this area lies in the field near Molland Methodist chapel. It is marked by a slight depression in the ground at SS 812283. If this is indeed the site it is on a hill brow, and the engine contemplated may possibly have been a Newcomen engine. When the Molland Tithe Map was completed in 1843, field 423 of Bremley Tenement on the valley floor by the ford was described as 'The Copper Mines Piece' and indicated the surface area of the mine. Production in 1845 was 134 tons of copper ore and the following year 3. By 1850, the compiler of *White's Directory of Devonshire* could record 'There is a copper mine here but it has been closed during the last three years'.

In its 1857 edition *Billing's Directory* stated,
About a mile from the village are two copper mines: the old one, about 70 fathoms deep, is full of water, but the new one, which is about 26 fathoms deep, and consists of yellow and grey copper is being worked with considerable success by a London firm. Mr Thomas Bennett(s) is captain of the mine.[27]

The new mine, which had been underway since 1881, began its operations at Bremley but then transferred its operations to a site to the south of Gourt Farm in the next valley. A description of the Molland mine in the mining section of *Kelly's Directory* of 1856 clearly describes the old workings.[28]
The mine is held under a lease, at a royalty of 1/15th, granted by Sir Robert Throckmorton, Bart of Buckland ... The known lodes on the sett are the main and the north ... it consists of quartz, carbon of iron, and yellow copper ore ... There have been six shafts sunk. The South Shaft is sunk 30 fathoms; the engine shaft is sunk 62 fathoms. There are the following levels in this shaft;–
the adit level is driven 60 fathoms;
the 20-fathom level is driven 50 fathoms;
the 30-fathom level is driven 80 fathoms east and 60 fathoms west;
the 42-fathom level is driven 57 fathoms east and 42 fathoms west;
the 52-fathom level is driven 46 fathoms east and 23 fathoms west;
the 62-fathom level is driven 30 fathoms east.
The mine is worked by water-power. The wheel is 36 feet in diameter, 2 feet six inches breast in the water, and 6 feet stroke. There is a crushing machine. The mine is drained by 8-inch bucket and 9-inch plunger. The

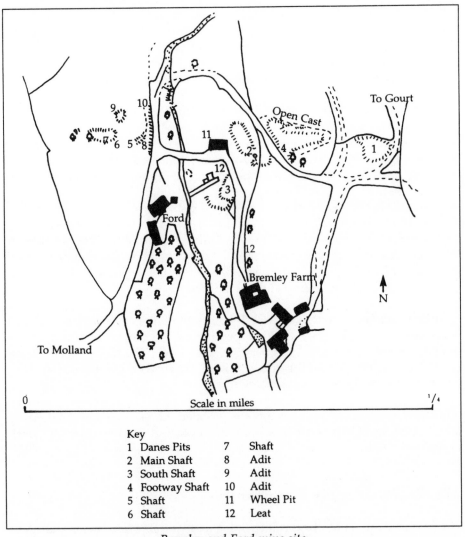

Bremley and Ford mine site.
Based upon the Ordnance Survey 25in. Plan of 1888.

Key
1	Danes Pits	7	Shaft
2	Main Shaft	8	Adit
3	South Shaft	9	Adit
4	Footway Shaft	10	Adit
5	Shaft	11	Wheel Pit
6	Shaft	12	Leat

minerals found in this sett include yellow and grey copper ore, and a small portion of silver. This mine is now worked for copper ore. The company consists of 10,000 shares ...

A succession of reports in the *Mining Journal* show that the working had been underway since 1851. Space permits only certain key references here. In December of that year the Engine Shaft was down to 42 fathom level, ore was on its way to Swansea and the new crusher was about to be put to work (*M.J.* 20-12-1851). The following April, apart from work in sinking the engine shaft and the 42 fathom level, work was in progress on constructing a dam to impound winter water in order to supply the wheel during the 'dry season'. Three old shafts were being cleared on the western hill with a long term possibility of these being sunk to connect with a westward extension of the new workings in order to improve ventilation and drawing (*M.J.* 10-4-1852).

As the 1857 *Billings* entry testifies, the move to Gourt had taken place before 1857. This site was similarly dogged by an unreliable water supply and in September 1857 work began in preparation for the installation of a steam engine (*M.J.* 19-9-1857). The shaft was cut down and timbered and an engine house built. By early November, it was roofed and the masons were building the boiler house (*M.J.* 14-11-1857). By the end of the month, the engineers were at work installing the engine, the shears over the shaft had been hoisted and the capstan was in the course of erection (*M.J.* 28-11-1857). In early December the engine, a Sims Combined Cylinder of 7in./14in. and one of the three smallest of that type known,[29] was pumping under the direction of Mr Loam the installing engineer (*M.J.* 5-12-1857). By the end of the month the engine was drawing but was unable to hoist and pump at the same time.

Williams' Mining Directory of 1862 describes the mine as 68 fathoms (124m.) deep, employing 36 persons with a payday on the second Saturday in the month. The mine remained in operation until 1867. The *North Devon Journal* (28-11-1867) advertised an auction of mining materials on 10 December. The Gourt site has never been worked since.

In 1878 *Harrod's Directory of Devonshire* reported the reopening of the Bremley mine. The object was not copper ore, however, but an iron working which lasted until 1894.

The Molland Copper Site Remains

The field evidence at Molland is interesting and viewable from roads and rights of way. Two buildings survive. Working eastwards from Molland village the site of the Copphall Shaft (SS 812283) is in the field behind the Methodist chapel – an almost indistinguishable dip and hump of a shaft on the east side of the hedge opposite Moor Lane. It is clearly shown as a disturbance on the six inch map of 1891 (Devon XVI S.W.). At Ford and Bremley a combination of open working, former shafts and levels appears as a disturbance running across the valley. The flooded main 70 fathom (128m.) shaft is next to the (working) leat a short distance south of the point that the water runs under Roach Hill. The Danes Pits shafts were at Gourt Cross (SS 819283). They are marked by a filled in depression to the left of the farm gate. The shafts and levels of Gourt mine appear near the ruined building and dumps in the valley below the farm (SS 823283).

There is a restructured building (SS 818283) next to the track leading towards Bremley Farm from Ford. This was formerly a smithy building, certainly for the iron ore company and possibly earlier. The wheel pit lies next to the stream on the other side of the track.

The Gourt Mine Engine House

Of the surviving mine engine houses in the Exmoor area, that at Gourt, 2 miles east of Molland village, is the most unusual. A small and unassuming building, it has a shape and form not normally associated with such structures. However, despite its size and appearance, it housed a small Cornish beam engine, the only application of steam as the prime source of power in the copper mines of North Devon and a key feature in the final phase of working at the Molland Copper mine.

By the 1850s copper mining at Molland, active since at least the early years of the eighteenth century, was concentrated in the valley immediately north of Bremley farmhouse. Water from a shaft 62 fathoms (111m.) deep was pumped by means of a 42ft (12.6m.) diameter waterwheel which, in 1856, was reaching the limit of its power. Lateral development had failed to find further workable deposits of ore and the only chance of continued operations on that site was by deepening the shaft. That required the installation of a larger, more powerful, water wheel or a steam engine; but the prospects below the 62 fathom level did not justify the expense.

There was, however, a promising shallow working on the same lode complex, a quarter of a mile to the east, where a shaft, 230 metres south-east of Gourt farmhouse, had been sunk to 20 fathoms (36m.) below a shallow adit and drained by means of a horse whim and kibbles. With the prospect of maintaining production from shallow depth, the Molland Mining Company decided to develop this as their new engine shaft and abandoned that at Bremley.

Water was not readily available at the new site so, in July 1857, the company advertised for a small steam engine adapted for both pumping and winding. That chosen was a second-hand Sims combined cylinder beam engine, with 7 inch and 14 inch cylinders, supplied and erected by Mathew Loam of Liskeard in Cornwall. Although not as popular as it had been in the 1840s, this double-acting compound arrangement, identical to that used at the Knap Down mine at Combe Martin, provided the flexibility to alternate between winding and pumping.

Housed in a tiny building about 20yds (18m.) north-west of the shaft, the engine was mounted on an integral frame carrying the beam and flywheel.

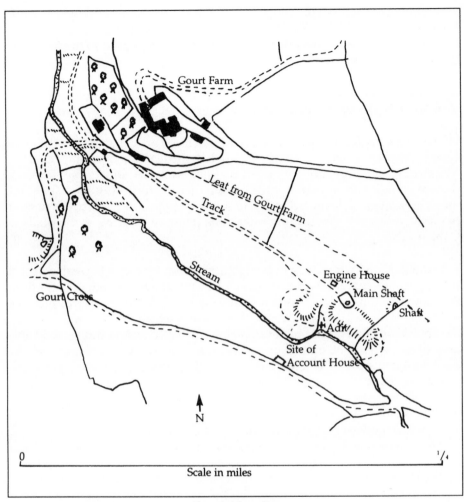

Gourt mine site.
Based upon the Ordnance Survey 25in. Plan of 1888.

There was, therefore, no bobwall required to support the beam, as with the Sims engine at Knap Down. The four walls of the house were required only to support the roof, with strengthening on the lower south-western wall to withstand the forces put on it by the winding drum. The flywheel shaft extended through that wall and carried the pinion driving the crown wheel on the winding drum axle.

The engine house is a ruin today. There is no trace of the chimney which stood to the north as it was demolished in the late nineteenth century. Neither are there visible remains of the boiler house on its north-eastern side, although recent excavation work has uncovered a portion of the masonry bed for the

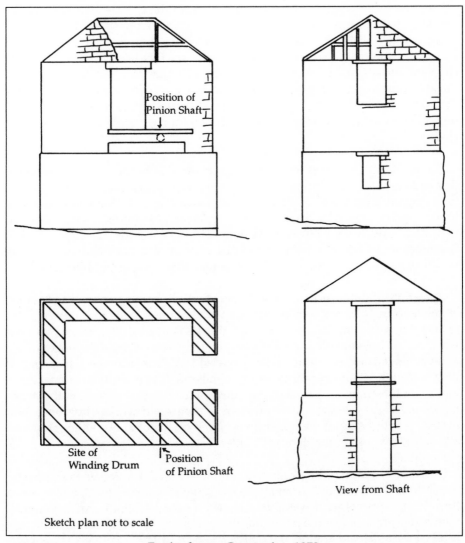

Position of
Pinion Shaft

Site of
Winding Drum

Position
of Pinion Shaft

Sketch plan not to scale

View from Shaft

Engine house, Gourt mine, 1972.

boiler. However, sufficient survived in 1971-72 to allow a reconstruction.

Substantial mountings outside the house carried the winding drum itself. This was covered with timber boarding, protecting it from the wind and rain. Hinges, for doors on the shaft side, could be seen fixed in the stonework at the southern corner of the engine house. Set in the south-western wall is a substantial timber block which carried the pinion shaft. Staining from the grease lubricating the bearings can still be seen on that timber.

The setting of the engine house well back from the engine shaft allowed the winding chain to run over a pulley on a frame above the shaft. Power to the pump rods in the engine shaft was transmitted by a short run of flat rods, probably taking their motion from a crank geared to the flywheel. To the north of the shaft was the site of the original horse whim, a circular plat partially cut into the hillside, a similar cutaway to the north east being for the capstan used to move the pumps in the shaft during maintenance. The rope drum was housed in a pit now evident as a depression in the centre and a rope gully aligned with its shaft.

Completed in December 1857, the engine was within three months working day and night to cope with the work load, but it proved extremely adaptable to the company's purpose. With occasional modifications to the pitwork, it was found capable of pumping water from a depth of 72 fathoms (130m), plus that raised by hand from a winze 10 fathoms (18m) below the 72. In addition it wound some 1200 tons of ore plus the vast amount of deads and dressing waste which is now heaped around the shaft, before abandonment in 1867.

Operations did not proceed without incident, as there were breakages in the engine and the pitwork which necessitated temporary halts to pumping. But by far the worst mishap occurred on the 15 February 1861 when, without warning, the boiler exploded killing two workers who were in the boiler house at the time. Eliza Pearce was partially buried by debris from the explosion and died within the hour. Her companion John Bennets was badly scalded, lingering on for fifteen hours before dying. Eliza, aged fifteen, worked on the dressing floors whilst John, at sixteen, was an underground worker, but what their reason was for being in the boiler house we shall never know, although it was a haven of warmth in the depth of winter.

This was no ordinary breakage and it took two weeks to repair the boiler, by which time the water had risen above the 32 fathom (59m.) level, and it was a further ten days before it was pumped clear of the 52 (95m.). An eleven inch hole had been found in the boiler but there was no sign of corrosion; although it was a second-hand engine, the boiler was new in 1857. Perhaps the engineman at the time, John Dunn, had allowed the water level to drop too low. The water supply to the engine was by way of a small leat (an extension of that to Gourt Farm) and it was notorious for running dry in summer but was unlikely to do so in midwinter. No reason for the failure was ever given and enquiry into the incident did not proceed beyond an inquest – inspection of coal mines and their associated plant had been in force since the 1850s but it was not until 1873 that it was applied to metal mines.

Unassuming the engine house at Gourt might be, but close examination will reveal the evidence of its former use. That it survived for so long is due to its

Wheal Eliza mine, c.1912. Vowles

Wheal Eliza mine : present-day view. Exmoor National Park

Inside Honeymead mine, showing stone arching at the entrance. M. Atkinson

Raleighs Cross mine, 1905. Hole Collection

Langham Hill mine c.1870, showing the aerial ropeway. James Date

Colton West Adit ore bins, 1908. Hole Collection

Timwood Level, c.1908. Hole Collection

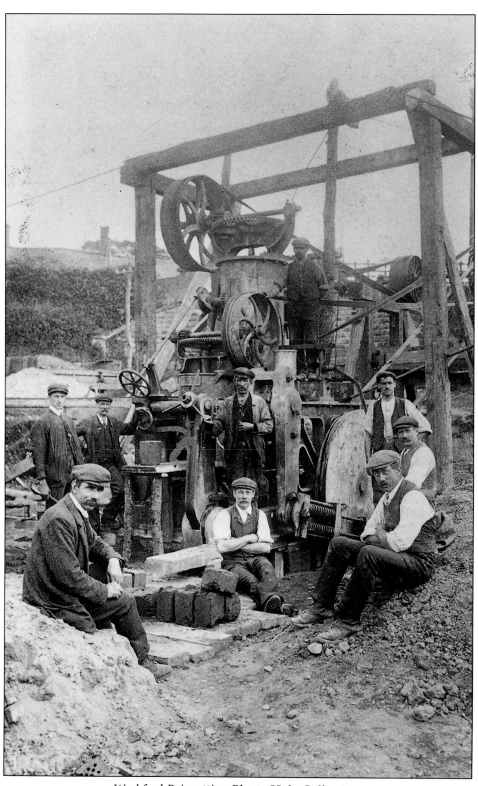

Washford Briquetting Plant. Hole Collection

Burrow Farm engine house, before conservation work by the National Park.
M. Atkinson

Remains of the ore crusher house, Bampfylde mine. Exmoor National Park

adaptability to agricultural use, unlike the larger engine houses. Now it has been allowed to fall into ruin but, with stabilisation and protection, what remains could stand as a monument to the final phase of two centuries of copper mining in this quiet Devon parish.[30]

Mining Technology

Mining technology is closely linked to a three-stage process identified by Schmitz as follows.[31] Firstly, the easily accessible ores at shallow depths requiring minimal technical input are exploited. Secondly, less accessible ores are sought requiring greater technical input. Thirdly, the more remote and less rewarding ores are worked in a struggle for survival, necessitating much greater technological input.

Water Power

This is well illustrated by the Bampfylde mine site. The earliest descriptions by Thomas Cletscher show a productive site without drainage problems. The only technical input was a hand gin not in service. By 1725, and for all subsequent workings, pumping was a priority. In the inventory of 1868 six waterwheels are mentioned, indicating a high level of water-powered mechanisation. Ultimately a steam engine was installed on No. 4 Shaft. At the same time the crusher house installed in the mid century and Captain Pope's Jigging Machine installed shortly before 1870 are signs of attempts to reduce costs and maximise yield.

In the light of this general picture the evidence of copper working at North Molton and Molland offers a good opportunity to examine the contribution of water power and the dressing process in more detail.

When Henrik Kahlmeter visited the Heasley Mill mine site in 1725 he reported seeing two pumping engines on either side of the valley. The western engine was powered by a 30ft (9m.) waterwheel. A double crank was attached to its stock. At either extremity of this two rods, each 4 fathoms (7.3m.) long, were attached and when one end of the crank was raised the other extremity, and its attached rods, were depressed. Both rods reached 4 fathoms below ground. These worked 'two pump spears down in the mine, each 16 fathoms deep'. The water thus forced up was by pipe from each pump into a single large pipe which ran to the adit. Kahlmeter made a useful sketch of this engine in his diary.

The eastern engine was of the same design but was powered by a 24ft (7.3m.)

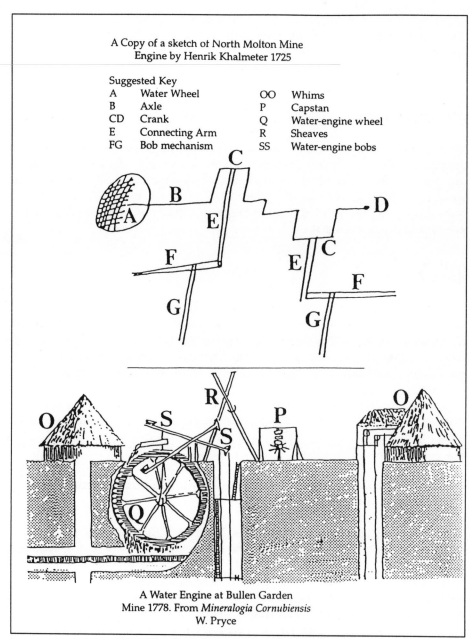

A Copy of a sketch of North Molton Mine
Engine by Henrik Khalmeter 1725

Suggested Key

A	Water Wheel	OO	Whims
B	Axle	P	Capstan
CD	Crank	Q	Water-engine wheel
E	Connecting Arm	R	Sheaves
FG	Bob mechanism	SS	Water-engine bobs

A Water Engine at Bullen Garden
Mine 1778. From *Mineralogia Cornubiensis*
W. Pryce

North Molton mine engine, 1725.

wheel and had a modification involving two half wheels which is hard to envis-age without a sketch, but was probably a steadying device. It seems almost certain that these engines were similar to those shown by Pryce in his *Mineralogia Cornubiensis* on his section of Bullen Garden mine.

In Blake's section of 1772 the isolated deep bottoms in the eastern part of the North Woods mine were pumped by a chain and churn pump.

When the same mine was to be reopened in the first decade of the nineteenth century the famous engineer John Rennie was invited to design a wheel to pump it dry. His specifications still exist in his letter books in the Institution of Civil Engineers but unfortunately they do not include the plans originally enclosed. Briefly, he proposed a 55ft (17m.) waterwheel of 8ft (2.4m.) width, he anticipated a very slow motion that precluded the use of cranks and suggested gearing instead. This would take the form of placing 'segments on the rim of the waterwheel to work a spur wheel or pinion on the shaft of the crank'. The segments were to be placed in the middle of the waterwheel, having buckets 4 ft (1.2metre) wide on either side. The crank thus activated was to work the pump at eight strokes a minute. The pumps were to have a barrel of 15 in. diameter and were to raise the water 45 fathoms (83m.) in two lifts. Whether this proposal was ever implemented is unknown.

Later in the century the auction of the Prince Albert mine included a 50ft (15.2m.) x 5ft (1.5m.) waterwheel, and a 24ft (7.3m.) x 3ft (1m.) waterwheel.[32]

The inventory of 1868 lists no less than six waterwheels at work on the mine with one 50ft (15.2m) wheel taken down and requiring repair.

The main engine wheel was 50 feet in diameter and, apart from its duties in the eastern workings, it drove the pumps on No. 4 Shaft. The power from the wheel on the valley floor was transferred by a system of flat rods leading across the valley and up the hillside to the shaft collar. They were supported on a series of rollers on pivoted arms. The 1868 inventory details this as follows:
172 fathoms 2 inch best Iron Rods, from Pumping-wheel to No. 4 Shaft, with Pullies and Stands: also Holding down Fend-off and shaft bobs.

The system worked best when the wheel was in direct line with the shaft. This was the case on the Bampfylde mine and the line could still be detected in April 1979 by a dip in the dumps and the remains of wooden bases for the pivoted arms preserved on the hillside.[33] The holding down, fend-off and shaft bobs were large weighted boxes. They acted as counterbalances to assist upward and downward direction. In Cornwall similar lines of flat rods running for quarter of a mile were not uncommon.

The loss of power in transmission was clearly considerable. By the mid nineteenth century the potential efficiency in the traditional waterwheel had been taken to its limit. One solution to this was 'shammelling' and this arrangement seems to have been adopted on the Bampfylde No. 4. Under this arrangement one engine operated the pumps in the lower part of the mine while another was responsible for the remaining lift to adit level. A horizontal steam engine was installed on No. 4 Shaft responsible, as the 1868 inventory states, for pumping and drawing.

A similar but much shorter run of rods also connected the pumping wheel to the Engine Shaft pumps. Waterwheels were situated well clear of shaft collars as a precaution against flooding the workings.

Molland mine was similarly water powered but was dogged by another problem of water power – insufficient water, particularly in summer. A solution being considered in 1852 was the impounding of winter water in a reservoir higher up the valley. Eventually the answer was the installation of a Sims steam engine in 1857.

Dressing

The dressing process was an essential element in copper mining. Its aim was to ensure that the maximum amount of ore and the minimum amount of waste rock was sent to the smelter in Swansea. Traditionally women and children as well as men were employed on the dressing floors. Apart from stamping engines, known since the sixteenth century at least, the processes were unmechanised until the eighteenth century.

Ore brought to the surface was washed and sorted by size and quality. The lumps of pure ore (prills) were withdrawn, ore mixed with other vein minerals was sent to be 'ragged'. This involved men breaking it down with 10lb hammers before it was passed to be 'cobbed' by girls with special long headed hammers. The remaining mixed ore was then crushed by girls with bucking hammers working on flat iron slabs. The powder from the bucking sheds was then 'jigged'. This involved placing the material on a sieve that was moved up and down in the water and allowed to settle. The relatively coarse copper ore settled near the bottom, above was a middle layer which was re-treated by bucking and jigging; the top layer was waste. The fine ore escaping through the sieve was treated in buddles. This involved ore stuff being passed down a sloping board in a stream of water. There were parallel ridges across the flow of the water. The material was allowed to settle here and the layers containing ore collected.

Kahlmeter in 1725 mentions 'stampers' among the workforce implying the use of a stamping machine. Copper is very friable and not well suited to stamps. An excellent alternative was discovered by John Taylor of Wheal Friendship in 1796 improvising with two discarded pump pipes. This was

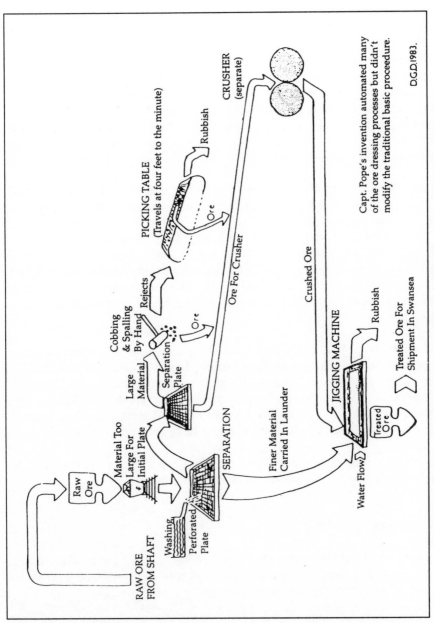

Flow diagram to illustrate the operation of Captain Pope's new Jigging Machine and Picking Table. The Bampfylde mine circa 1870.

developed into the crusher rolls. Ruins of crusher houses are to be seen on the Bampfylde mine.

The crusher was housed in a two-storey building attached to the pit of the waterwheel that powered it. The crusher was housed at first floor level and was served by a hopper into which the uncrushed material was passed. Once crushed it was collected from below and withdrawn through a door at ground floor level. The crusher rolls needed to be kept in tension but also needed to allow potentially damaging, very hard material to pass through. This was achieved by a crank arm held in tension by a weighted box suspended from it outside the crusher house. It is this arrangement that gives the crusher house building shells their most distinctive feature, a small aperture in the wall opposite the door on the ground floor allowing the exit of the crank arm.

The 1861 census for Molland names five women, four of whom are described as dressers or workers at the copper mines (one is described inaccurately as a 'miner' since no women worked below ground). They are Eliza Pearce thirty-three, Mary Yearndle forty-two, Anne Pike thirty-two, Elizabeth Pike forty-four and Elizabeth Bowden seventeen. From the findings of the 1842 Children's Commission it is possible to suggest that they lived a relatively healthy, if rather raw life in the open-sided dressing sheds. If they escaped silicosis by working on the surface, working in often cold and wet conditions they must later have been prone to rheumatic problems.

Towards the end of his reign on the Bampfylde mine, Joseph Pope invented and installed his Jigging Machine and Picking Table. A model of it is held by the Royal Albert Museum, Exeter. Its aim was to mechanise the dressing process as far as possible. Its appearance and operation are demonstrated in the accompanying diagrams. Given that it was installed during the fading years of the mine's copper phase its efficacy can never have been properly tested.

Thus, despite innovation and invention, the copper mines were unable to avoid the inevitability of disadvantageous market changes.

The Location of Sites

All sites are on private land and are not accessible without permission. Some are viewable, at a distance, from public rights of way. Any visitor is advised to check an Ordnance Survey map in the first place.

Footnotes

1. Lysons Correspondence. Microfilm of British Ad. Manuscripts 9430. West Country Studies Library, Exeter. p.291.
2. *Mining Journal*, 17-7-1852, p.347.
3. *Mining Journal*, 19-6-1854, p.412.
4. *Mining Journal*, 1-7-1854, p.427.
5. *Calendar of Five Rolls*, Vol. 5, Edward III, 1337-1347. p.4354.
6. H.C. Darby, *An Historical Geography of England*, 1936, p.258.
7. See H. Dines, *The Metalliferous Mining Region of South West England*, 1969, pp.770-1.
8. William Rees, *Industry Before the Industrial Revolution*, 1968, p.472.
9. *Letters and Papers of Henry VIII*, Addenda 1528, Vol. 1, No. 622, p.207.
10. N. Molton Parish Registers, Devon & Cornwall Record Society, West Country Studies Library, Exeter.
11. Devon Record Office, 1786/A and /PO2.
12. Public Records Office E190.
13. Liverpool University Library, Rhys Jenkins Papers M.S.7.1. (21) (Thomas Cletscher) and M.S.7.1.(23) (Henrik Kahlmeter). Both are rather raw translations of material in the Swedish Bergs Collegium archives.
14. William Pryce, *Mineralogia Cornubiensis*, 1778, p.278 and Plate IV.
15. David Dixon, 'Mining and the Community in the Parishes of North Molton, South Molton, Molland and Twitchen,' Southampton University M.Phil. Thesis 1983
16. Lysons, *Devonshire*, pp.cclxxiv and cclxxxv.
17. Devon Record Office 261 OM/FS.
18. *Mining Journal*, 25 May 1852, Britannia Prospectus.
19. Mining Records Office (AMR 86C).
20. Morris, *Directory of Devonshire*, 1820, p.380. See also R. Burt, *British Ore Preparation Techniques* p.380.
21. Dixon 'Mining and the Community,' Thesis, 1983.
22. Thomas Westcote, *A View of Devonshire in 1630*, 1845, p.65.
23. Throckmorton Papers, Shakespeare Birthplace Trust, Stratford-upon-Avon, Item 503.
24. Henrik Kahlmeter, 'A Relation of the English Mines in 1725' Rhys Jenkins Papers, Liverpool University Library.
25. Jeremiah Milles Papers. Molland. Questionnaire on Devonshire Parishes 1747-1756. Bodleian Library.
26. Throckmorton Papers, Item 695.
27. Billing, *Directory of Devonshire*, 1857, pp.276-7.
28. Kelly, *Directory of Devonshire*, 1856, p.xxix.
29. D. B. Barton, *The Cornish Beam Engine*, 1969, p.112.
30. This section uses material from various sources including the *Mining Journal*, *North Devon Journal*, abandonment plans originally deposited with the

Mining Record Office and now in the Devon Record Office at Exeter, the Throckmorton Papers in the Shakespeare Birthplace Trust, Stratford upon Avon, information gathered from local residents by Roger Burton and the results of excavation by the Exmoor Mines Research Group.

31. Christopher Schmitz 'Capital Formation and Technological Change in South-West England Metal Mining in the Nineteeth Century,' *Exeter Papers in Economic History*, No.9, 1978.

32. *Cornwall Royal Gazette* 18 April 1845. Sale Notice re: Prince Albert mine.

33. Dixon 'Mining and the Community'. Thesis, 1983, pp.251-252.

Bibliography

Burt, R., Waite, P., Burnley, R., *Devon and Somerset Mines, 1984.*

Delderfield, Eric R.,   *Just Wandering in Devon*, 1954.

Dines, H. G.,   *The Metalliferous Mining Region of South West England*, Vol 11, 1956.

Earl, Bryan,   *Cornish Mining*, 1968.

Lysons, Daniel,   *Topographical and Historical Account of Devonshire*, 1822.

Pryce, William,   *Mineralogia Cornubiensis*, 1788. Reprinted 1972.

LEAD AND SILVER MINING

Peter Claughton

Silver-lead mining on the borders of Exmoor has a long history, stretching back over seven centuries, but the visible remains are predominantly those of the last one hundred and fifty years. The surviving engine house ruin on Knap Down, with other features in and around Combe Martin, stand as memorials to nineteenth century activity, but these are amongst those mines whose peak years were well before the Industrial Revolution. Unfortunately little is currently visible from the earliest periods as much has been lost beneath more recent working.

The later remains may be the dominant features but from time to time the early evidence will come to light and we must be prepared to recognise it as a valuable link in our industrial history.

Combe Martin – The Geological Background

On the coast at the western extremity of the National Park there is extensive lead mineralisation, accompanied by zinc and small amounts of copper, occurring mainly within the Lester and Wild Pear Slates, which are rocks of Devonian age. These lead deposits, yielding high levels of silver, have been worked intermittently since at least the late thirteenth century. The major veins, or lodes[1], lie to the north and east of the village of Combe Martin, running east-west or south-east north-west, that is parallel with the main street, and underlying south. Lodes in the Knap Down area which varied from this trend were known as caunter lodes. They are crossed by a number of north-south trending crosscourses, some of which are themselves mineralised. It is at the junction, between the veins and mineralised crosscourses, that some of the richest ore deposits are found. The ores are primarily argentiferous galena (lead sulphide), although, in the upper weathered parts of the veins, cerussite (lead carbonate) occurs, along with pockets of tetrahedrite or fahlers ore containing very high silver values.

Early Mining – Medieval to the Early Sixteenth Century

It was the silver content of the veins which attracted the interest of the Crown and royal privilege was exercised over all such ores. The Combe Martin mines were therefore worked by the Crown or its appointees until the privilege was removed in the late seventeenth century.

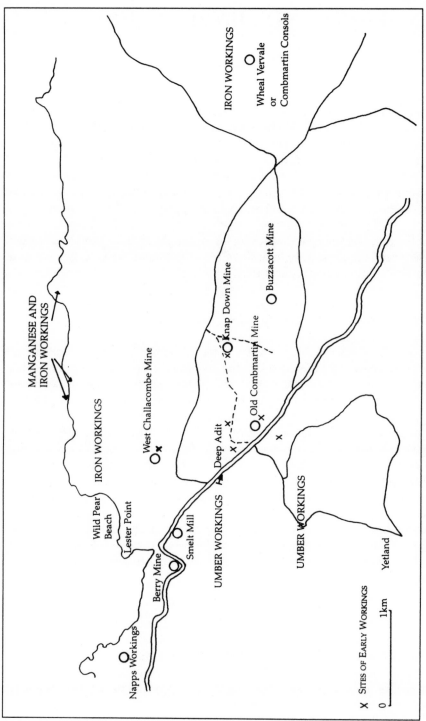

MANGANESE AND
IRON WORKINGS

IRON WORKINGS

Wild Pear
Beach

Lester Point

Napps Workings

Berry Mine

Smelt Mill

West Challacombe Mine

UMBER WORKINGS

Deep Adit

Knap Down Mine

Old Combmartin Mine

Buzzacott Mine

IRON WORKINGS

Wheal Vervale
or
Combmartin Consols

UMBER WORKINGS

Yetland

X SITES OF EARLY WORKINGS

0   1km

Combe Martin's principal Silver-Lead mines and sites of other mineral workings.

Unlike the multiplicity of small independent producers, governed by customary law, which dominated the lead mining areas of Mendip, North Wales, Derbyshire and the Pennines, the mining of silver-bearing ores was, by medieval standards, centralised and highly capitalised. Having established the mines in the last decade of the thirteenth century, the Crown kept tight control over their working. A management structure was introduced under the Keeper, a Crown officer, who was himself monitored by the Controller, another Crown appointment. Day-to-day operations were the responsibility of the Supervisor, with the miners and ancillary workers employed on either day wages or piecework.

Initially in 1292, and frequently thereafter, the Combe Martin mines were worked in conjunction with those at Birland (Bere Ferrers) in South Devon, collectively known as *Minera Regis in comitatu Devon* (the King's Mine in Devon) but on occasions they would be worked as separate units. The South Devon mines were by far the larger, with production frequently overshadowing that of Combe Martin. In fact, within three years of being opened the Combe Martin mines had ceased production after smelting only a small quantity of lead. Exactly why the mines were closed so quickly is uncertain, for they subsequently proved to be rich in silver, but the reasons may have included difficulty in smelting the ores.

Devon silver production was then centred on Birland alone until 1325 when the Combe Martin mines were again mentioned, at that time independent of those in the south. However, they do not appear to have been a profitable prospect for the Crown was happy to grant them, and 'all issues and profits arising therefrom', to Adam de Strode for a rent of 20 marks (£13.30) per year. In the following five years the mines changed hands five times; even the lord of the manor, Phillip de Columbariis, attempted to work them in 1327-28. This rapid turnover gives every indication of mines in which the readily accessible ore had either been worked out or presented insurmountable problems.

It was not until 1360 that the mines were worked successfully, over a period of four years producing £788 in silver. This pattern continued throughout the late-medieval period, with short periods of intense working followed by years of relative inactivity. Continuity did improve by the nineteenth century, but it would appear that in six hundred years no one period of continuous productive working exceeded seventeen years.

Silver-lead mining tended to be at the forefront of medieval technology. The demand for silver coinage was such that the best methods available were utilised to work what was a restricted resource. When troubled by water or lack of suitable ore for smelting, the lead miners in areas like Derbyshire and the Pennines would move on to open up fresh sources close to surface. As silver bearing ores were found in only a relatively few locations it was necessary to work deeper and treat ore which would have been rejected elsewhere.

The large outlay in the Devon mines on capital works – adits, deep shafts, pumps and the smelting complex needed to gain access to and treat the silver bearing ores – ensured some continuity of working if not production. This is particularly noticeable in the working of the Birland mines, production leaders for much of the fourteenth and fifteenth centuries. However, as output there fell, it appears to have stimulated renewed interest in Combe Martin. Production which may have appeared small in relation to that in later years was of considerable importance to the English economy and by the early years of the sixteenth century the mines were apparently regarded as the most promising in the South West. Continental technology introduced at that time, however, proved no better than that available locally in developing that promise.

The last reserves of accessible, shallow, rich ore were worked out at the end of the sixteenth century, but only after smelting difficulties had been overcome using techniques born of a scarcity of suitable lead ores on Mendip. Attempts to get under and drain the old workings by long adits and later by steam power were to occupy the next two hundred and fifty years.

The only evidence of medieval mining visible today is the earthworks marking the sites of shallow shafts along the outcrop of some veins. These can best be seen along Harris's Lode, north of Corner Lane (SS 589465), although they are not spectacular, with many years of husbandry having softened their lines. There is also evidence of an ancient adit alongside the lane to the south-west of Silver Mines Farm (SS 594466). Ancient underground workings are known on a number of other veins, clearly identified in the reports of nineteenth century mining companies on Knap Down, at West Challacombe, Lester Point, and closer in to the village east of the fire station and north-east of Castle Street, with others adjoining Coneypark Lane. However, as yet insufficient is known to date these workings accurately.

Working methods were initially simple. A shallow shaft would be sunk on the vein to gain access to the ore, which would not necessarily occupy the whole of the vein, being often disseminated through a matrix of waste material or present as a string of varying width. This body of ore would be followed later-ally as far as crude transport and ventilation would allow, the whole process being repeated a short distance along the vein. These early outcrop workings were shallow, limited by the drainage technology available. Leather buckets were used to bail out accumulated water and haul it to the surface using hemp ropes. As the ore body was followed deeper, short underground shafts, or winzes, were sunk following the dip of the vein, and large numbers of men were employed just to haul water up those shafts.

Adits were known in the Devon mines as early as 1297 and water percolating from surface as well as that lifted from the lower workings was channelled through to them on wooden launders, with great savings in labour and an extension to winter working, but these adits were themselves initially very shallow by modern standards. A long drive through barren ground to gain an increase in depth was a costly and time-consuming business without the aid of explosives. Fire setting, which involved heating the rock with a brushwood fire until it split or shattered and then removing it using picks and wedges, was the common method of breaking ground, although the softer shales would yield to the pick alone. However, an adit of a hundred yards in length was recommended at Bere Ferrers in 1327, and an adit of that length would have been of considerable advantage on the high ground in the area of Harris's Lode.

Pumps were available by the fifteenth century, in the form of tree trunks bored out to form the body. By the late sixteenth century, a depth of 32 fathoms (57.6m.) below surface was achieved in the Fayes mine and an ancient manually-operated forcing pump was recovered in the nineteenth century from 24 fathoms (43.2m.) below the surface of the gardens immediately west of the Great Orchard. Here the vein had been worked out to surface, although there is nothing visible today.

The Seventeenth and Eighteenth Centuries

There is evidence for at least two shallow adits driven north-east from the River Umber towards areas of ancient workings, but it was not until the mid seventeenth century that a deep drainage adit was started. The deep adit, with its entrance (SS 583467) near the Pack of Cards Hotel, has all the hallmarks of the work of Thomas Bushell, the Crown lessee in the 1640s. Commencing as a shallow cut-and-cover drain across the low lying ground, it entered the rising ground to the east of the hotel before turning south-east as a relatively barren drive of nearly half-a-mile in length to reach the main area of old workings between Castle Street and Corner Lane. Bushell did not complete the adit, and it is not until the early nineteenth century that we have evidence that it reached the old workings. Shafts for ventilation and haulage were sunk at regular intervals along the back of the adit. The sites of the majority of these are now lost although two were utilized in the nineteenth century and can be identified. One of them, that later known as William's, was 4ft (1.2m.) by 5ft (1.5m.) in section and twisted out of true vertical as sunk. Up this whim shaft were hauled all the deads, or waste rock, removed in driving the adit forward towards Harris's Lode, which is cut 40 fathoms (72m.) below surface. The deep adit is no longer accessible, and has doubtless collapsed along much of its length, but it still affects the drainage of the area between Castle Street and Corner Lane.

For the silver-lead mines in Devon, the eighteenth century was a quiet period. There were occasional attempts at reworking Combe Martin but the readily accessible ore was gone. With low lead prices, even some encouraging assays of the silver content gave no justification for deep working. Prices did increase at the end of the century and in 1813 an attempt was made to unwater the old workings using a 20ft (6m.) diameter waterwheel. This proved quite inadequate and, with lead prices falling again, it was abandoned in 1817.

Old Combmartin Mine

Although there was some interest in the 1820s, it was not until the mid-1830s that the market was again favourable and another attempt was made, this time using steam power. In 1835 the Combmartin and North Devon Mining Company opened up two mines – at Knap Down and in the area between Castle Street and Corner Lane.

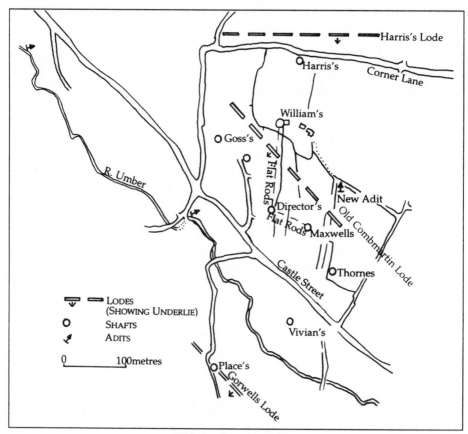

Old Combmartin mine.

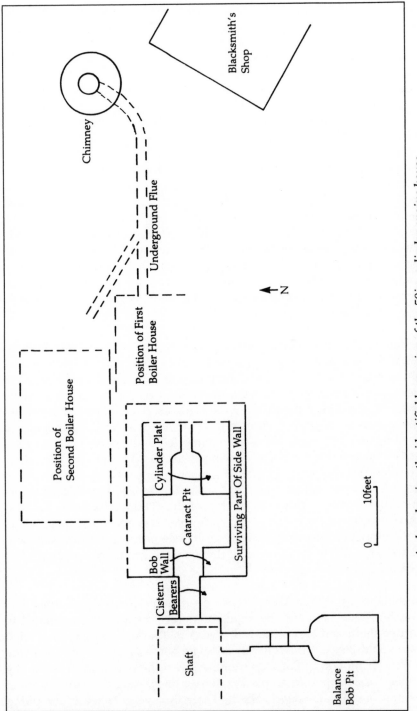

A plan showing the identifiable remains of the 50in. cylinder engine house, William's Shaft, Old Combmartin mine.

The latter, usually known as the Old or Old Combmartin mine, was to be worked by two engine shafts: William's, where a 50in. cylinder Cornish engine was erected, was the old whim shaft on deep adit enlarged and deepened with the intention of cutting Harris's Lode below the 27 fathom level;[2] Director's (SS 588463), was the engine shaft of the 1813-17 working, cutting the Old Combmartin Lode at about the 50 fathom level. Power for pumps in the latter was transmitted from the engine at William's by means of flat rods. Initially pumps were also installed in the main winding shaft, Maxwell's, in the gardens west of the Great Orchard, again powered by flat rods.

Whilst steam power for pumping had been available through much of the eighteenth century in the form of the vertical cylindered beam engine, it was inefficient, requiring large quantities of coal all of which had to be imported into the South West – that supplied by the small anthracite mines in the Bideford area was not suitable for steam-raising. It was, therefore, restricted to situations where a good return was assured on the investment, principally tin and copper mines. Innovations made by Watt in the latter part of the century, subsequently improved by Cornish engineers, increased efficiency and, allied to the increase in lead prices, made its use at Combe Martin a viable proposition.

The engine installed at William's had a cylinder of 50in. (1.25m.) internal diameter, with a piston making a 9ft (2.7m.) stroke in the cylinder, translated by the beam into an 8ft (2.4m.) stroke of the pump rods in the shaft. Steam from the boiler was admitted to the cylinder above the piston powering the indoor stroke and thereby lifting the pump rods in the shaft. Cutting off the steam before the piston reached the end of its travel took advantage of its expansive effect to complete the stroke. Valve gear connected to the beam controlled the supply of steam and opened ports allowing steam to exhaust to the condenser on the outdoor stroke. In a normal single acting application, the weight of pump rods would cause them to fall in the shaft, working the pump plungers and returning the engine piston to the top of the cylinder ready for the next cycle. Any excess weight in the pump rods, over and above that required to operate the plungers, was compensated for by one or more balance bobs, and the rods were massively constructed of the longest pitch pine available, up to 11in. square.

The installation at William's was, however, more complicated than this. There was from the beginning the requirement for power to be transmitted to the other two shafts and only a short lift of sinking (bucket) pumps was needed in William's Shaft itself. Consequently an angle bob was erected alongside the shaft to transfer motion to flat rods running down the hillside. These 9in. by 6in. wooden rods, supported on pulleys, took a line through where Danycraig Cottages now stand to Director's Shaft. There they were linked to the pump

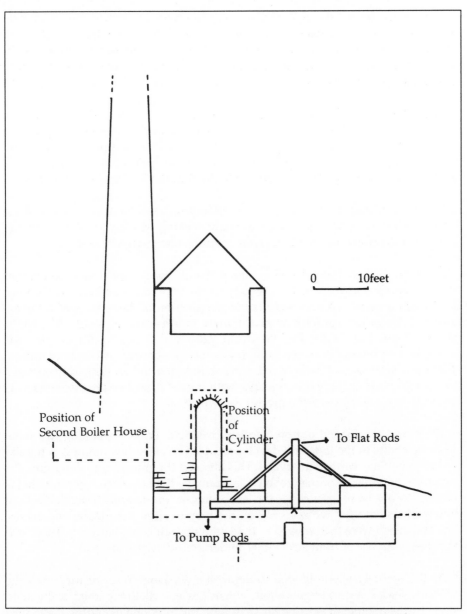

0   10feet

Position of
Second Boiler House

Position
of
Cylinder

To Flat Rods

To Pump Rods

50in. cylinder engine house. William's Shaft, Old Combmartin mine.
Reconstruction of western elevation showing angle/balance bob.
Due to the hillside location the engine house has deep foundations
and consequently a two storey cataract pit.

rods and then turned through 90 degrees at another angle bob to run on a trestle bridge across Rock House Farm garden to Maxwell's, a total distance of 196yd (180m.). Balance bobs at the two shafts would have compensated for the weight of both pump rods and flat rods, leaving the engine to lift only that sufficient to operate the pump plungers and overcome friction in the flat rod pulleys.

Vertical shafts had probably been introduced at Combe Martin in the late eighteenth/early nineteenth century, breaking with the medieval practice of irregular deep shafts following the underlie of the lode, stepped so as to allow manual haulage, a practice still used in the North Molton mine in the seventeenth and eighteenth centuries and illustrated in the 1772 section of that mine.

Vertical working shafts required good planning, based on a knowledge of the character of the orebodies, unfortunately lacking at Combe Martin as the bottom of the mine had not been seen since the late sixteenth century.

As the company drained and explored the old workings, it became evident that the upper portion of a rich orebody on the Old Lode had been worked out by the old miners. This orebody lay at the junction of the lode, with a mineralised crosscourse running approximately north-south through Maxwell's Shaft. Opened up below the old workings, it was found to dip towards the south-east, following the steep underlay of the crosscourse. All ideas of sinking William's Shaft to cut Harris's Lode were abandoned and working concentrated on the Old Lode, leaving the company with the liability of an engine which was some distance away from the productive workings.

The mine was opened out on Cornish lines, with crosscuts linking two main working shafts to the lode and development levels extending along it at regular 10 fathom (18m.) vertical intervals. This allowed the company to determine the economic boundaries of the orebody, and remove it by overhand stoping, that is cutting the ore away from above the level, after the ground had been blocked out into sections between winzes sunk on the lode to allow ventilation and access. Ore and deads were then moved to the winding shaft using barrows. There was apparently no use of tramways either underground or at surface.

As the orebody was followed in depth the workings were further from the working shafts. A new engine shaft, Vivian's, was sunk to the south of the main street by deepening an existing air shaft with the intention of cutting the lode at the 127 fathom level. However, it was found that the lateral extent of the orebody diminished in depth, such that it was only a few fathoms long at the 102 fathom level, at which depth the new shaft was abandoned.

A new steam engine was probably planned for Vivian's Shaft but never erected, a water pressure engine being used to drain the shaft during sinking,

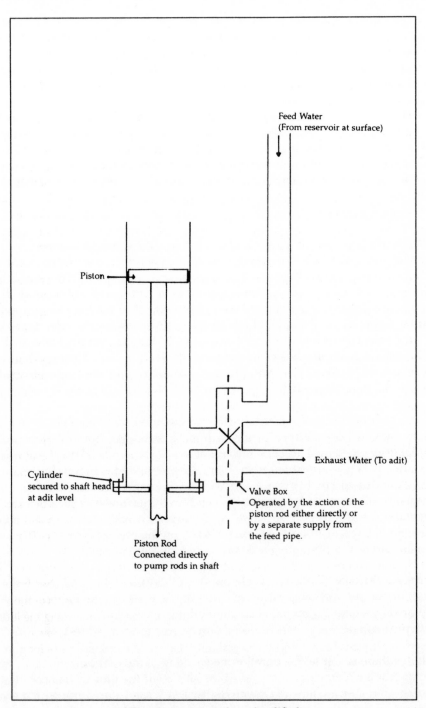

Water pressure engine, simplified.

and later lifting water to the level of the pumps in Director's. Water pressure engines were unusual in the South West, although used extensively in some upland lead mining areas. To operate satisfactorily, they required a good head of water, (around 150ft [45m.] minimum) operating on a reciprocating piston in a cylinder, in this case of 7in. (17.5cm.) internal diameter, with valve gear controlling the supply and exhaust in much the same manner as a steam engine. The engine itself was installed at deep adit, allowing the exhausted tail water to run off at that level. Arrangements at surface for the feed water to the engine are unclear as no surviving evidence has been identified. Water from the River Umber could not provide sufficient head, so it is likely that an existing supply, to the pond east of William's Shaft, was utilized. A head of 150ft could be achieved by feeding the water down the hillside and into the shaft through a continuous pipeway.

Whilst the low cost, simplicity and efficiency of the water pressure engine had probably favoured its introduction, it proved a liability in the winter of 1845-46 when the deep adit collapsed. The engine, and consequently the sinking of Vivian's Shaft, had to be suspended for four months until the adit could be cleared and the exhaust water allowed to run off. That calamity also drowned out the lower levels on the Old Lode as the engine at William's was not capable of lifting the full inflow of water the further 27 fathoms (48.6m.) to a shallow adit. This was despite moves to improve efficiency when William's Shaft was sunk to the 27 fathom level and pumps installed to take the strain off the flat rods as the mine deepened.

A number of the development levels were extended north-west and south-east along the Old Lode in anticipation of further orebodies, but without success. Exploratory crosscuts had been put out at the 27 fathom level on either side of the lode. That to the north, used in channelling water to the pumps in William's, was extended to cut Harris's Lode without finding workable deposits. The crosscut south-west under the valley, on which Vivian's was originally sunk for ventilation, was directed so as to come under ancient working adjacent to Coneypark Lane. There an old shaft, Place's, on the underlie of Gorwell's Lode was cleared out. Although at least one new lode was cut under the valley, from which a small amount of ore was raised, the old miners were found to have removed virtually all the workable ore from Gorwell's. Ground to the north-west, under old workings north and east of the present Fire Station, was also explored by extending an old adit. But nothing of consequence was found and, with the main orebody worked out, the mine was abandoned in 1848.

Today there is ample evidence for the working of the Combmartin and North Devon Mining Company. Around Maxwell's Shaft the ground has reverted to gardens, but they are now at a much higher level than before, sitting on the vast quantity of deads brought up the shafts using a steam whim. This whim was the only mechanised form of winding used on the mine. With a 14in. (35cm.) internal diameter cylinder it was a double acting engine, in which the steam was applied alternately to either side of the piston, powering both strokes and allowing the engine to be reversed easily. An exact location and layout for the whim is not known, and there is no evidence for a building surviving on site. A typical arrangement would have had a vertical cylinder and beam, as a pumping engine, but with the outer end of the beam connected by a sweep rod to the crank on a flywheel, the latter geared to a drum carrying the heavy winding chain. As the engine was a small one, it is possible that it was an 'all-indoor' arrangement, as used for the 7/14in. engine at Gourt, Molland Mines, with cylinder, beam and flywheel enclosed within the engine house.

Winding at all other shafts was by means of the horse whim, the rope or chain being wound round a large wooden drum on a vertical axle, supported in a wooden frame, and turned by one or two horses. This method had been used for centuries and occasionally would be used to power pumps, as during the clearing of Place's Shaft. The physical evidence where it survives is a level circular area, perhaps with the axle bearing stone at its centre, a short distance from the shaft. One such winding shaft, Thorne's, is marked by a substantial spoilheap in the south-western corner of the Great Orchard. Spoilheaps here, at Director's, Vivian's and the other shafts, are now heavily overgrown or grassed over, allowing them to blend into the surrounding gardens.

However, not all the owners allowed the tipping of deads and dressing waste on their land. Substantial stone walls were erected to retain the spoil around certain gardens, clearly seen in a narrow strip immediately west of the Great Orchard, and behind Rock House where they are heavily buttressed.

On the hillside above Danycraig Cottages, part of the southern wall of the engine house still stands on the east side of William's Shaft. Here the foundation of the bobwall, massively constructed to support the beam, has recently been exposed, as has the angle bob pit, widening at its southern end to accommodate the balance box required once pumps were installed to the 27 fathom level. North and east of the engine house were two boiler houses, with underground flues leading to a chimney 23 yards (21m.) away, adjacent to the blacksmith's shop. Only one boiler was installed in 1836, although two were planned, and when, in 1841, increased steam raising capacity was required to cope with pumping below the 57 fathom level, a second was erected. A crude cut-and-cover flue was linked into the arched masonry of that from the first boiler house.

William's Shaft itself is currently open, revealing the ragged outline of one side of the old whim shaft as it twisted out of alignment with the enlarged, and cleanly picked out, engine shaft.

During working by the Combmartin and North Devon Company, the area to the east of William's could have been described as the nerve centre of the mine. Besides the key pumping engine and the blacksmith's shop there was the account house – Southdene now occupies the site and is probably based on that building. From this vantage point, the mine captain could survey the activities spread out to the south around Maxwell's Shaft. Immediately in front was a small waterwheel-powered set of stamps, used in breaking up the ore for the dressing process, and alongside it was the pond, which provided an adequate supply of water to the wheel and to the steam engine for use in cooling the condenser. After a new set of stamps were attached to the whim engine at Maxwell's, the pond water was also available for the water pressure engine. Infill has now obliterated all evidence. This is unfortunate as the area had probably been used during earlier workings and could be the site of the 20 foot pumping wheel used in 1813-17. Certainly the leat which fed water onto the site, along the line of Watery Lane, crossing Corner Lane and then following the contour of the hillside around Tree Tops, has all the appearance of being an ancient cutting.

After 1848, the Old Combmartin Lode was never worked again in an organised fashion. That part accessible above deep adit was picked over by tributers, (independent miners paying a small royalty to the mineral owner) and there was much talk of reopening, but fragmented ownership was a stumbling block to the acquisition of a consolidated sett.

There was a misguided attempt to rework Harris's Lode and the area immediately south of it in the 1870s, based on the mistaken belief that the Old Lode had been displaced by the mineralised crosscourse at Maxwell's and that an extension of the orebody would be found to the north closer to Harris's Lode.

The only tangible evidence for this working is the New Adit, a shallow cross-cut in the north-western corner of the Great Orchard. This is still open and gives access to stopes on a minor lode. Harris's Shaft, 40 fathoms deep and originally sunk to cut the lode at 15 fathoms below the surface, was reopened. Small amounts of lead and zinc ores were raised. The zinc ores, having been left by earlier miners, were by the latter part of the nineteenth century a marketable product. No pumping was required as the deep adit still drained the workings to 40 fathoms below surface, and winding was by means of a simple windlass, the collar of the shaft being enclosed within a small building. Even with high lead and zinc prices, it would have been difficult to make this venture pay. As it was, prices were declining rapidly and the workings were abandoned in 1880.

Knap Down Mine

Exploration at Knap Down by the Combmartin and North Devon Mining

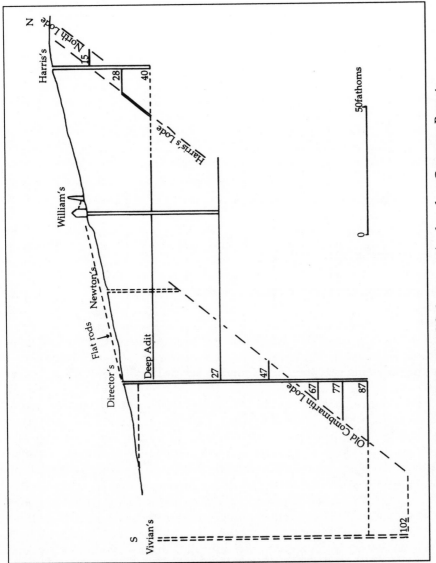

Combe Martin, 1848. Simplified cross section based on Company Reports.
Level depths in fathoms below Deep Adit at Director's or surface at Harris's.

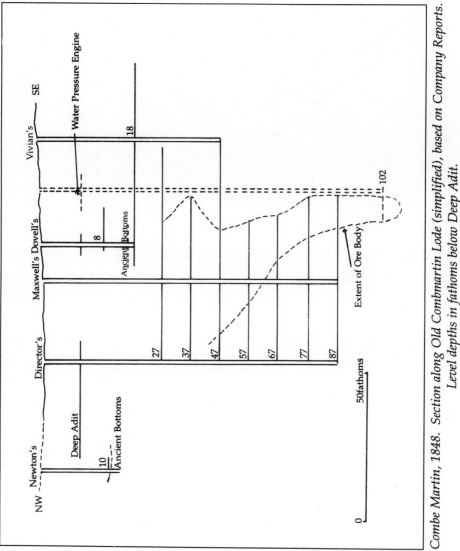

Combe Martin, 1848. Section along Old Combmartin Lode (simplified), based on Company Reports. Level depths in fathoms below Deep Adit.

Company in the 1830s indicated some promise. However, it was not until a reduction of royalties was negotiated in 1842 that it was worked seriously. Using only a horse whim and kibbles (large egg-shaped iron buckets used for hauling ore, deads and water), the mine was initially drained down to the ancient bottoms at 50 fathoms (90m.) below surface. Lateral development required a mechanised form of pumping. With little surface water available on site, steam power was chosen and a 26/50in. combined cylinder Sims engine was erected early in 1843, reputedly built by Lewis of Redruth. However, productive working only lasted three years before the mine was abandoned.

The site today is dominated by the ruin of the Sims engine house (SS 596466). Built partially into the slope of the ground, allowing the larger cylinder to be installed below the floor, it belies the fact that it housed such a tall engine. In this compound arrangement the two cylinders were mounted vertically, one above the other, sharing a common piston rod. Steam passed from the smaller to the larger cylinder allowing maximum use of its expansive power. This double acting arrangement was ideal for whim engines. When used for pumping only, a large weight was attached to the piston in the smaller cylinder, adding to its power on the indoor stroke, the weight being lifted on the outdoor stroke by the action of the large cylinder.[3] A single boiler of 10 tons was housed

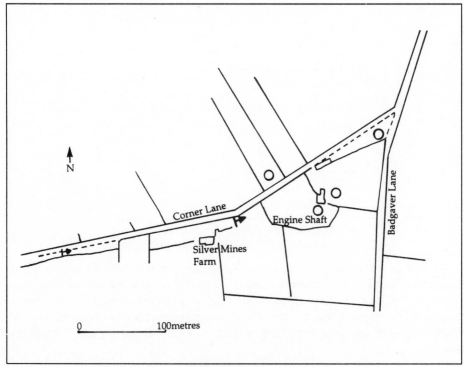

Knap Down mine.

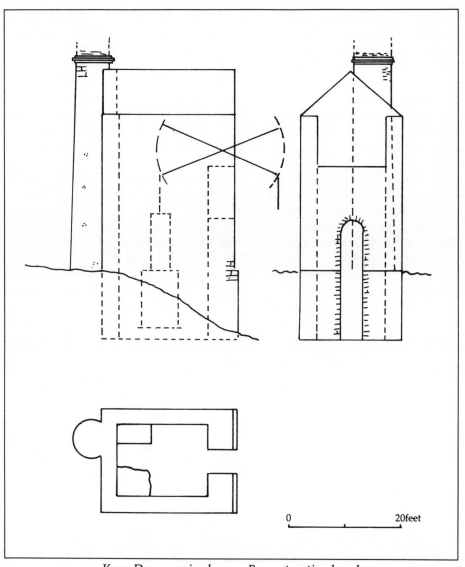

0 _____ 20feet

*Knap Down engine house. Reconstruction based
on examination in 1971, showing position of cylinders.*

to the east of the engine, the chimney being incorporated into the rear wall of the engine house. The beam arrangement was the same as that of the 50in. engine at William's but the pitwork was uncomplicated with only two lifts of pumps in the engine shaft, the lower one being a bucket lift, essential to remove water from the sump at the shaft bottom and that above an 8 in. diameter plunger.

90

In fact, the Sims engine was oversize for the task in hand, being nearly as powerful as that at William's. The company would have expected the engine shaft to be sunk much deeper to work deposits similar to that at Old Combmartin, but Knap Down was to remain a shallow mine and the engine was only required to work part of each day to keep the workings clear of water.

When the company also abandoned the Old mine in 1848 the plant there and at Knap Down was sold, at least one lift of pumps from the former being bought by the Wheal Eliza company on Exmoor. The Sims engine was in the course of being dismantled when the mine was taken on lease by a new company. After re-erection, the engine served two companies which were short lived, and in 1859 was set to work for the North Devon Silver-Lead Mining Company.

This Berkshire-based company worked Knap Down for three or four years with little success before it was discovered that development levels had been driven on a minor branch of the main lode and richer ground was only a few fathoms away. Production increased to a point where the mine was meeting its costs. Working eastwards into ground on the Buzzacott estate, a number of new veins were found. At the junction of two of these was a particularly rich orebody. These sustained the mine for a number of years before it was again abandoned as worked out in 1868. Exactly what happened after that is unclear. The company was not wound up until 1873, and there are indications that steam power was still in use on the site in the 1890s, when prospecting was being carried out. Oral evidence collected locally also suggests the use of a steam whim at the mine in the late nineteenth and early twentieth centuries, perhaps as late as 1927 when prospecting was again under way, although supporting documentary or archaeological evidence has yet to come to light. Certainly, the Sims engine was not removed from the site until broken up for scrap long after the demise of the North Devon Company.

Apart from some work in the Vale of Girt, the majority of surface activity at Knap Down was confined to a small triangle of ground between Badgaver and Corner Lanes. There are, however, ancient workings under the area north of Corner Lane. Surface working on the Buzzacott estate, east of Badgaver Lane, was specifically precluded in the company's lease, although a dispensation was granted for a shallow shaft sunk in Middle Furze Park. A complex pattern of lodes occurs in this area and at least seven were worked within 220 yards (200m.) of the engine shaft. All produced ore at shallow depths, the rich orebody of the late 1860s being found at the 10 fathom level.

The location of the site on a broad hilltop made the use of adits for deep drainage a difficult proposition. A shallow adit, driven from east of Silver Mines Farm, cut the engine shaft only a few fathoms below surface. There was no effective deep adit although three or more attempts were made. The earliest

91

was the adit alongside Corner Lane, west of the farm, which was cleared out in the 1790s but never completed, although it had the advantage of following the main lode and would have drained the mine to 20 fathoms (36m.) below surface. Most ambitious, and potentially the most effective, was the intention of the Combmartin and North Devon Company to continue the Old mine deep adit along Harris's Lode in the direction of Knap Down. An adit from the Vale of Girt was planned in the early 1860s but, as the lode discovered there did not prove particularly promising, it was abandoned. The only attempt carried to any length was that made later from the area of Beara Farm.

Once abandoned, the dumps around the Knap Down engine shaft were thoroughly picked over for any scraps of ore that might remain, the engine house was robbed for building stone, and spoil was removed for road mending, destroying much of the dressing floors and other surface features. The shallow adit has been used as a source of water for the adjacent farm. Today, access to the site is somewhat restricted, but it has the potential for detailed archaeological investigation and interpretation.

Other Ventures Around Combe Martin

Whilst the Old Combmartin and Knap Down mines were the only important nineteenth century producers in the area, there were other ventures. Some were determined efforts to reopen ancient workings in an attempt to emulate the apparent success of the two productive mines, whilst others merely took advantage of improved lead prices to attract capital into activity which had little chance of success, as happened in the 1870s. Amongst the latter were the Yetland mine; South Combmartin (SS 587460) – an attempt to rework Gorwell's Lode with even less chance of success in 1879, prices having fallen steadily for four years; Parracombe (SS 667449), where there was some limited working near the malthouse and in the valley to the west; the reopening of Harris's Lode already mentioned; and activity at West Challacombe between 1873 and 1878, when at least three companies were involved.

The mine at West Challacombe, generally worked in conjunction with Lester Point, was probably active in the late medieval period. A group of old workings in the former orchard, alongside the stream south of the farm, are now largely obliterated, but a short distance downstream are the spoilheaps from an adit (SS 584473). Known as Meadow Level in the 1870s, this was driven as a crosscut to intersect a series of east-west lodes. The spoilheaps display the irregular shape characteristic of having been tipped using hand barrows, but that is not necessarily a sign of great age as tramways were little used at Combe Martin.

Three of the east-west lodes outcrop in the cliffs between Lester Point and the beach at Combe Martin, where they were worked by adits driven at or near the high water mark. Although the cliffs in this area have been eroded, the adits can still be identified, as can Shacrey Shaft, sunk in 1843-44 on rocks a little above high water below Lester Cliff, and the stone-arched entrance to an adit on Wheal Path Lode at Wild Pear Beach. This latter adit was planned as a tramway level by the New Combmartin Silver Lead Mining Co. Ltd in the 1860s, but like so many other companies working the sett its activities lasted only a few years.

On the west side of Combe Martin Beach, at Newberry (SS 573471), and at Napps (SS 563477), about half-a-mile further west, silver-lead ores were worked from at least the early 1800s under various titles – Berry mine, Wheal Harmony, Wheal Basset, and finally (1859-62) as Great Watermouth mine. The site of an old shaft can be seen alongside the road up Newberry Hill, originally connecting with an adit driven west from the lower end of Berry Lane. At Napps the spoil heap from a shaft reputedly 35 fathoms (63m.) deep could be identified in the 1970s close to the old coast road, as could an adit about 16yd (15m.) above the beach at Golden Cove. In the 1860s, the mine at Newberry was being worked at the 20 fathom level without any mechanised form of drainage beyond a horse whim and kibbles. A waterwheel and pumps were planned but there is no evidence they were ever installed.

In the area of Buzzacott (SS 602460) east of Combe Martin village, various trials were made in the nineteenth century. A shaft and adit to the west of the lane to Beara Farm, apparently on a vein crossing the valley south of Buzzacott House, may be the site of earlier workings, but the later, speculative, activity was in two crosscut adits driven towards the north. The entrance to the lower adit is marked by water rising in the bed of the stream 110yd (100m.) south of Beara Farm with a large spoilheap to the south of it, on the east bank of the stream, now levelled to form part of the gardens for Buzzacott House. This adit was driven slightly west of north for 315yd (288m.), with at least two air shafts, in an attempt to explore ground east of Knap Down mine. At a much higher level, the other crosscut was driven in a northerly direction with similar intentions. The entrance is marked by a moderately sized spoilheap 361yd (330m.) north-east of Beara, composed mainly of soft shales. It is doubtful if either adit achieved its aim of cutting productive lodes. Trials for silver-lead have been made as far east as Martinhoe. Most, like that at Parracombe, were minor but a small mine was worked on the Combe Martin-Trentishoe boundary in the 1840s and 1850s. Known as Wheal Vervale (SS 625465) and, later, as Combmartin Consols, it employed water power to work to a depth of 20 fathoms (36m.) below adit.

The site of the waterwheel used by Combmartin Consols in the 1850s can be identified on the north side of the stream, 492yd (450m.) west-south-west of Tittiscombe, by the remains of the tail-race culvert. This 40ft by 3ft (12 by 0.9m.) wheel pumped an engine shaft 256yd (234m.) to the north-north-west by 2in. diameter iron flat rods. The site for an earlier wheel used by Wheal Vervale is unclear. This wheel, constructed of oak, 36ft in diameter with only a 23in. breast (10.8 by 0.575m.), was of a type long out of fashion by the 1840s and could have been inherited from a much earlier working. It was located close to the engine shaft and geared to a drawing machine, or whim, in addition to a short run of flat rods working the pumps. Its narrow breast is an indication that only a limited flow of water was available, brought on to the site from a nearby pond using wooden launders. Artificial ventilation of the mine was by means of a water blast, unusual in the South West, in which water was allowed to fall down a large pipe in the shaft, carrying air with it which was collected in a receiver and directed through pipes to poorly ventilated levels. The fall of water was probably achieved by turning the tail-race from the wheel down a pipe in the engine shaft, the receiver being located at adit level where the water could run off with that from the pumps.

A number of small spoilheaps marking shafts and adits can be seen midway between Lower Verwill and Tattiscombe farms, although those to the north are connected with iron rather than silver-lead mining. There is also a long shallow trial adit driven north from Tattiscombe. Being worked entirely by water and horse power, there were few substantial structures on this mine to survive the 135 years since abandonment.

Dulverton and Brushford

Lead and zinc mineralisation is also found as isolated occurrences in a broad band roughly following the boundary between rocks of Devonian age and the Culm Measures, from Barnstaple in the west to Dulverton in the east. Generally these were low in silver, but sufficient was present in ores found in the Dulverton-Brushford area at the beginning of the fourteenth century to attract Crown attention.

The Dulverton workings have subsequently been known as 'silver mines' but, other than in a few exceptional instances, assays revealed the silver content to be only 4 to 6 ounces per ton, well below economic recovery prior to the mid nineteenth century. Until the removal of Crown privilege on base ores containing precious metals, in the Mines Royal Acts of 1689 and 1693, the law on mines containing small amounts of silver was unclear. By the seventeenth century, however, the consensus was that to be a mine royal the value of the silver should exceed that of the base metal, in this case the lead. Nevertheless, in the 1670s, when lead was being worked on Sydenham and Ashford lands on the

Dulverton-Brushford boundary (possibly in Allers Wood), they were still held to be mines royal despite low silver assays. During the early part of the eighteenth century, the Sydenhams worked the mine at Combe for silver at a considerable loss.

There were short-lived attempts to revive the mines in the nineteenth century, with Morgan Morgans, late of the Brendon Hills mines, reopening that at Beer (SS 891275) in 1867. There, an adit and two shafts with the remains of a small blacksmith's shop could be seen a few years ago. Of earlier activity here and south-eastwards towards the River Barle, little is visible today, although an exhaustive search will reveal perhaps five further sites of shallow working.

In a group of trees 109yd (100m.) west of Beasley Farm, two shafts are marked by overlapping shaft mounds (SS 918269), formed from the spoil tipped around the shaft collar and its subsequent collapse when abandoned. These shafts were shallow and are unlikely to have connected with the adit, the entrance of which is now lost, driven from the riverside to the east. At Combe the reputed site of the mine lies immediately south of the house (SS 912266). Much is now under an ornamental pond, but heavily overgrown ground to the east of the drive exhibits signs of shallow working. Lead ore is in some cases found in association with the lenticular limestones, both being worked on the same site, as at Gulland and Cole Wood (SS 897263). At the latter site, 437yd (400m.) south-east of Knowle, the workings were primarily for limestone in two narrow, roughly parallel, quarries with, at the eastern end of the northern quarry, a large shaft mound as evidence of lead mining.

Ore Preparation

Once raised to surface the silver-lead ores had to be prepared for smelting, an activity known as dressing. In its simplest form, this was by manual separation – hand picking the pieces of clean ore from the waste material. Where ore and waste were intermixed, it was broken up with heavy hammers of stone or iron, the latter known as buckers, and again picked over by hand. What remained was broken smaller and washed in a shallow inclined trough through which a stream of water flowed carrying off the lighter waste and fine ore, the larger heavier pieces of ore being left on the floor of the trough.

This process changed little from the medieval period through to the sixteenth century. It was impossible to smelt the fine ore efficiently prior to the latter half of the sixteenth century, so much was allowed to go to waste. But as improved smelting technology became available, early waste heaps were rewashed, destroying much of the physical evidence of early dressing activity, and specific sites have yet to be identified at Combe Martin.

With the new smelting technology came improvements in dressing techniques. Jigging the crushed ore and waste on sieves in large water-filled tubs allowed the heavier ores to settle to the bottom with the waste, being lighter, collecting near the top and being discarded, whilst the fine ore and waste fell through the sieve. The fine material was then subjected to further gravity separation on the buddle where it was passed over a shallow inclined surface in a stream of water, the ore settling first and the waste being carried away in much the same manner as it had been in the medieval period. However, varying the incline and water flow allowed recovery of the majority of the fine ore. Contamination of silver-lead ores with other metallic minerals of similar specific gravity made separation a difficult operation requiring considerable skill. Dressing operations became far more complex than can be described easily in these few pages, and the reader is directed to Burt's *British Ore Preparation Techniques* (1982), for more detail.

From the medieval period through to the sixteenth century, and much later in the case of small mines, dressing was carried out close to the workings, all that was required being a suitable stream of water. But, as the processes became increasingly mechanised, dressing was centralised in specific areas close to a source of power. At the Old Combmartin mine, the dressing floor was finally established in the area of Maxwell's Shaft, and that at Knap Down was adjacent to the engine shaft. At the latter, the scarcity of surface water was overcome by installing an extra lift of pumps in the shaft to raise water to a short adit very close to surface from where it ran over a waterwheel powering the stamps before being used for dressing purposes.

Silver-Lead Smelting Prior to 1600

Throughout the medieval period the silver-lead ores were smelted on sites near the mines. The early smelting hearths were simple affairs, known as boles. Constructed on exposed hilltop sites, they reduced the ore in a brushwood fire using the wind as a natural draught. They had their limitations, relying on the wind remaining in one direction for sufficient time to allow complete reduction. They were also only capable of dealing with sulphide ores (galena) of around walnut size or larger; anything smaller did not react properly, caking up in the hearth.

The later boles, used in Derbyshire in the late fifteenth and early sixteenth centuries, were large structures producing up to 16 fothers (about 17 tons) of lead at one firing, but documentary evidence suggests that those used in Devon in the medieval period were very much smaller. Walls of stone and/or earth were constructed on three sides, with the open side facing the prevailing wind. Logs, referred to as 'blocks', were laid across the base of the bole and covered

Remains of Knap Down engine house, 1971. P. Claughton

The former Combe Martin smelt mill, 1972. P. Claughton

Treborough quarry buildings c.1930, showing tunnel entrance (in the middle of the buildings). The building on the right is the mill. Hole Collection

Treborough new quarry c.1930. Hole Collection

*Treborough new quarry c.1930, showing tracks to tips and
(top right) the track from the adit and the incline to the mill.*

Inside Treborough slate mill, showing two cutting tables with overhead cranes.
Hole Collection

The earliest known photograph of Treborough quarry, probably pre-1914. Note the waterwheel (just visible bottom left) which powered the saws in the mill. Hole Collection

Limekiln at Heddon's Mouth. Exmoor National Park

Limekilns at the old Brendon Hill yard. M. Atkinson

John Brayley's workshop at Wade Mill, Molland. D. Warren

The former 'Exe Valley Wagon Works' of Charles Phillips, Bridgetown. D. Warren

A works photograph of one of the first Pool oil engines produced at Chipstable, c.1893. Museum of English Rural Life

John Chidgey (bearded) in his workshop at Watchet, c.1900.
Museum of English Rural Life

The pottery kiln in the garden of the Luttrell Arms Hotel, Dunster. Veryan Heal

The tannery buildings at Porlock. D. Warren

Heasley Mill, showing the woollen mill before it was partly demolished. B. H. White

Malthouse at Lynch, near Bossington. D. Warren

Wansborough Paper Mill, Watchet c.1910. Courtesy D. Warren

Watchet harbour c.1880. Hole Collection

The Quay at Minehead in 1906, showing (right background) the buildings of Lomas's sulphuric acid, glue and chemical manure works. Allerford Rural Life Museum

Porlock Weir harbour, 1907. Dovery Manor Museum

Countisbury Hill. Courtesy J. Bentley

Exbridge tollhouse, 1986. J. Bentley

The Brendon Hill Incline from Comberow c.1865, showing
temporary staging over a probable loading bay used when the incline
carried narrow-gauge track. Hole Collection

with a layer of slags, partly reduced ore from a previous smelting. Over this were placed layers of small branches, brushwood and the ore. A mass of brushwood was then set on the open, windward, side and ignited. Ore near the top of the bole was oxidised by being roasted in the heat and reacted with unroasted ore releasing the lead and liberating sulphur dioxide to the atmosphere ($2PbO + PbS = Pb + SO_2$). The lead, still bearing silver, collected in a hollow beneath or to one side of the bole.

Derbyshire practice was for campaigns of bole smelting at certain times of the year when the prevailing winds could be relied upon to be strong and continuous. This was not the case in Devon where the requirement for a steady supply of lead to the refiners meant that bole smelting continued throughout the year.[4] To counter changes in wind direction, a device known as the turnbole (*bolas turnellas*) was developed. The structure of the bole was mounted on a heavy wooden platform that could be rotated about a central vertical axle or post, allowing it to be moved to face the wind. These turnboles were substantial structures – when one was dismantled at Buckland Monachorum in South Devon in 1302 it took seven men a whole day in 'removing the post and timber of the said bole from the ground', for which they were paid 4d. each, twice the normal rate of labour – heavy work indeed.[5]

Much lead, and silver, remained in the slags after initial smelting and this 'blackwork' was treated in a charcoal-burning furnace with draught provided by foot bellows. But before it could be resmelted it had to be cleansed of any waste, that is any residue not containing lead. After breaking by hand using picks and bucking hammers it was crushed – a horse powered 'engine', a millstone running on edge, being used in South Devon. Washing the crushed blackwork in a trough, in much the same manner as ore, removed the lighter waste.

The furnace was also used to treat the carbonate ore (cerussite) and the smaller sulphide ore, increasingly so as the mines developed and the large ore became rarer. With its higher temperature, much lead was lost in the furnace through volatization but provided the silver content was high enough such losses were acceptable.

Early furnaces appear to have been small circular stone-built structures with two or three sets of bellows. With increased reliance on the furnace to smelt the smaller ore, there were developments principally in scale and adaptation to water power. Continental technology followed similar lines and when, in 1528, the 'German' Joachim Hochstetter erected a furnace at Combe Martin it was a substantial building taking its power from a leat running through the gardens, possibly alongside the River Umber. Hochstetter did not remain at Combe Martin long and there is no evidence that he successfully smelted the local ores.

It was not until the mid sixteenth century that new technology was developed in the lead industry on Mendip allowing greater efficiency in the smelting of the smaller lead sulphide ores, and it would be this, the ore hearth, which was successfully introduced to Combe Martin by Bevis Bulmer during the working of Fayes mine. Bulmer was responding to difficulties in smelting the Combe Martin ores, which may have prevented the working of some ores as early as the thirteenth century. The early closure of the Combe Martin mines at the end of the thirteenth century, the failure to work them successfully in the 1320s, and experiments with a liquation process in the 'hutt' during 1295-96 all indicate problems, possibly with copper contamination.

Our understanding of early silver-lead smelting is as yet limited, and for the late medieval period we must rely almost entirely on documentary evidence of a financial nature from South Devon. Some comparison can be made with fifteenth and sixteenth century Derbyshire practice where descriptive documents and some archaeological evidence are available, for, whilst the development of the silver-lead and lead industries should be considered separately, they shared a common ore base with a transfer of technologies, particularly in smelting, between them.

Unfortunately none of these early smelting sites at Combe Martin has yet been identified. The bole sites would have been on the high ground either side of the village, but the water powered furnaces needed a reliable water supply and would have been sited close in to the village alongside the river.

Refining

The product of smelting was a lead high in silver – fertile lead. To recover that silver it was necessary to refine the lead by cupellation – heating the lead in a blast of air created by bellows until it oxidised to litharge, leaving the silver alone in metallic form. This process remained virtually unchanged through the medieval period to the mid nineteenth century. Litharge resulting from cupellation was resmelted to produce a soft malleable lead suitable for fabrication, the manufacture of pipes, and roofing.

As with smelting, the locations of refinery sites at Combe Martin are not known, although their existence is recorded. In 1630 Westcote referred to 'divers monuments their names yet to this time remaining; as the king's mine, the store house, blowing house, and refining house'. A tantalising glimpse of what might be revealed by careful observation and archaeological investigation.

The Combe Martin and North Devon Smelting Co. Ltd

After the sixteenth century, there is no evidence for smelting or refining at Combe Martin until 1845, the ores mined being sent to large concerns in Bristol and South Wales. In that year, a mill was erected to smelt ores being raised from the Old Combmartin mine. The operating company, being independent of the mine, also imported ores through the tidal harbour, but with the closure of the mine this proved uneconomic and the smelt-mill closed down in 1851. Much of the mill building remains today (SS 577471) as part of Loverings Garage between Borough Road and the river, although it has recently lost its original pantile roof.

By the nineteenth century, the majority of lead and silver-lead smelting was carried out using the reverberatory furnace, developed towards the end of the seventeenth century, in which the fire was kept separate from the ore being smelted, allowing the use of coal as fuel. There was a number of variations – that used at Combe Martin, and throughout the South West, was the Cornish flowing furnace. This required the ore to be calcined in a separate furnace before it was smelted, and during the smelting process lime and iron were added to give a fluid slag which could be run off as waste when the furnace was tapped.

One flowing and two calcining furnaces were housed in the mill at Combe Martin along with two refining (cupellation) hearths and a reviver, a smaller furnace for recovering lead from the litharge produced in cupellation. All were constructed of firebricks held together with iron strapping, free standing within the mill building. The draught for all these reverberatory furnaces was provided by a chimney 65yd (60m.) above the mill and traces of the flue, of arched masonry, can still be seen on the hillside to the south-west. A small waterwheel was used to power the bellows for the refining hearths but its site is no longer

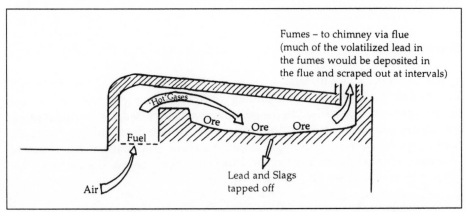

The Cornish Flowing (Reverberatory) Furnace as used at Combe Martin.

visible, much of the area round the mill building having been covered in tarmac or lock-up garages. Heavy black slags can be found in and around the river running through the site, although large amounts were reputedly used as road fill in the area.

Conclusion

With the preservation of industrial monuments increasingly a subject of public interest it is perhaps appropriate that this account should end with a description of what was for many years a functional building. The Combe Martin smelt-mill was capable of adaptation for other uses. The furnaces were not structurally part of the building and were easily removed. This left a long low building with ample floor space which had been put to a number of uses including the drying of umber (when a tall chimney was erected at its north-western corner), a saw-mill, and now a bus garage. Unfortunately, present usage has led to the loss of the original roof.

Whilst re-use can be an effective means of preserving buildings there is the danger that the new use will outgrow them. Engine houses on the other hand had little alternative use once the engine was removed. But even when robbed as a source of building material their substantial construction has allowed survival as ruined, but still prominent reminders of past mining activity.

An engine house, such as that at Knap Down, can be a focus for a renewed public interest in the past; but it should never be forgotten that beneath these prominent monuments to the nineteenth century there is hidden, often fragile, evidence of earlier mining and smelting. The medieval structures were ephemeral, often built of wood, leaving only a post hole or a scatter of slag as evidence of their existence, but such are the essential links with our early industrial past.

Sources

This account draws on material to be found in the Devon Record Office, Public Record Office (PRO), National Library of Wales, *Mining Journal*, and *North Devon Journal* and published in the books and articles listed for further reading. The reader is directed to those publications for the details in addition to the following specific reference to unpublished material. I am particularly indebted to Mick Warbuton, Roger Burton and Mike Gussin for access to their investigations in the area of the Old Combmartin mine.

Footnotes

1. For clarity the term vein or lode is retained for the silver-lead deposits at Combe Martin as they formed part of the terminology used by the nineteenth century miners. However they, and the iron/copper deposits in the East Buckland-North Molton-Molland area, are not true lodes, or infilled fault fissures, but lenticular deposits following the bedding of the country rock. The north-south crosscourses were the vehicle for low temperature mineralisation at a much earlier geological period than that in South Devon and Cornwall. For more detail see Durrance and Laming, *The Geology of Devon*, Chapter Six.
2. Unless otherwise stated, all level depths are below deep adit.
3. Where the weight was not installed and the larger cylinder used to power the plunger pumps on the outdoor stoke, as with the engine installed at Crofton on the Kennet and Avon Canal, the bearings for the beam on the bobwall were held down by long bolts recessed into either side of the wall. There is no evidence for such bolts at Knap Down.
4. In South Devon by the mid fourteenth century, as the amount of ore suitable for bole smelting diminished, smelting campaigns were introduced. A week at a time, three or four times per year.
5. PRO E101 260/22, translated by Peter Mayer for the Calstock parish archive sponsored by the Manpower Services Commission.

Bibliography

Burt, Roger,   *A Short History of British Metal Mining Technology in the Eighteenth and Nineteenth Centuries*, De Archaeologische Pers Nederland, 1982.

Claughton, Peter,   *The Combe Martin Mines*, publ. Combe Martin Local History Group, 1992.

Claughton, Peter,   'Mining in North Devon Prior to 1800', *Bulletin of the Peak District Mines Historical Society*, Vol. 11, No. 4, pp. 189-192, 1991.

Claughton, Peter,   'The Medieval Miner; a Preliminary Study' *Peak District Mines Historical Bulletin*, Vol. 12, No. 2, pp28-33.

Durrance, E.M. and
Laming, D.J.C. (eds),   *The Geology of Devon*, 1982.

Steam Power and Engine Houses
Barton, D. B.   *The Cornish Beam Engine*, 1969.

Share *et al*,   *Engine House Assessment*, Cornwall Archaeology Unit, Cornwall County Council, 1991 (particularly Chapter 3).

Ore Preparation

Burt, Roger,   *A Short History of British Ore Preparation Techniques in the Eighteenth and Nineteenth Centuries*, De Archaeologische Pers Nederland, 1982.

Smelting

Claughton, Peter,   'Medieval Silver-lead Smelting in Devon', in *Boles and Smeltmills*, ed. Willies and Cranstone, Historical Metallurgy Society Ltd, 1992, pp.12-15.

Keirnan, David,   *The Derbyshire Lead Industry in the Sixteenth Century*, Derbyshire Record Society, 1989, (particularly Chapters 2 and 4).

Percy, John,   *Metallurgy*, Volume III Parts 1 and 2, 'Silver and Lead', 1870, reprinted De Archaeologische Pers Nederland in association with Historical Metallurgy Society Ltd.

THE QUARRYING INDUSTRY

Andy Bowman and Chris Tilley

Quarrying has a history just as long as metalliferous mining, but has never attracted the level of research applied to its more romantic cousin. The written sources available to the historian are scarcer and production statistics in particular are few and far between, only being comprehensively produced after the main period of working of the Exmoor quarries. The first survey of quarrying was carried out by Robert Hunt, Keeper of the Mining Record Office, in 1854 but this was a unique survey and continuous records only commence when they become legally required by the Quarries Act of 1894. What do remain are the large-scale workings which, despite a certain extent of filling, form highly visible reminders of the industry in the landscape.

On Exmoor, stone of various types has been extracted, ranging from the more specialised slate, producing slates for roofing, cisterns and so on, through limestone mainly dug to provide lime for fertiliser, to gritstone dug for building and more lately for roadstone.

Methods of Extraction

In order to work any quarry, the overburden must be removed and, until the advent of mechanical methods in the late 1930s, this had to be done by hand. The material removed would be tipped outside the proposed quarry area and the amount could vary from only a few inches to tens of feet, depending on the geology of the site.

Prior to the general introduction of gunpowder, after the removal of the overburden any extraction would be by hand using picks, wedges, jumpers and, in some circumstances, firesetting.

By the end of the eighteenth century, gunpowder was in common use for both quarrying and mining and several methods were devised in order to use it properly to gain the maximum extraction of stone. One method used to remove material from the face and also to break up large pieces (popping) was to drill holes using a sledge hammer and a steel (or iron) drill or jumper and charge these holes with gunpowder and fuse. Before the invention of the safety fuse, the fuse was made from dried rushes or straw and inserted into the tamped gunpowder and this often led to accidents which were reported periodically in the press of the time. Handboring continued in the local quarries until the 1920s when steam drills were introduced and these were later succeeded by compressed air, allowing for a much larger take of stone.

Some quarries used a different method of loosening the stone and this was to drive a drift into the rock face for a distance, opening up the drift on either side to form a T-shape and charging the ends of the T with gunpowder or later with gelignite. This was then blown and produced a large amount of stone which could be further broken by 'popping', or by the use of sledge hammer and pick. This method of working is known to have been used at Beacon Down quarry near Parracombe, which was operated by Devon County Council until 1958.

The Slate Industry

The slate of Exmoor is of the Devonian Morte Series and generally of poor quality, especially when compared with the slates of North Wales and Cornwall. Nevertheless, for many years, quarries in the West Somerset area met a demand for roofing slates, slabs, lintels, water cisterns and gravestones. On Exmoor itself, a large quarry was worked at Treborough on the Brendon Hills and a small one at Chibbet Ford, near Exford, which belonged to the Marley family for some two hundred years and produced poor 'rag' slates (used for slate-hanging and some roofing). Numerous other small quarries are scattered all over Exmoor which produced slate for local use though little is known of their history. Outside Exmoor, two large workings were undertaken at Okehampton quarry, near Wiveliscombe, and at Tracebridge, near Wellington, with five other small workings at the Coombe quarries below Okehampton quarry.

All three main quarries had a similar pattern of development. The earliest workings date back several centuries – records date back to 1426 in the case of Treborough and 1608 for Okehampton. Sporadic working was undertaken at various times up to the mid nineteenth century, though scant records do not allow us to be specific about how often and for how long such small-scale operations took place. From the mid nineteenth century, demand for slate products rose with rapid population expansion and the quarries entered their main phase of working which lasted until the First World War. Okehampton quarry seems to have stopped just before 1914, but at Treborough and Tracebridge, activity continued until 1935 and 1939 respectively.

It is fortunate that the best documented and best 'preserved' quarry site is Treborough (ST 014368), lying as it does within the Exmoor National Park. The first reference to working here dates back to 1426 when Sir Hugh Luttrell ordered 2000 slates for Dunster Castle for a total price of 20d., which turned out to be half the cost of transporting them! In 1719, the quarry was being leased by

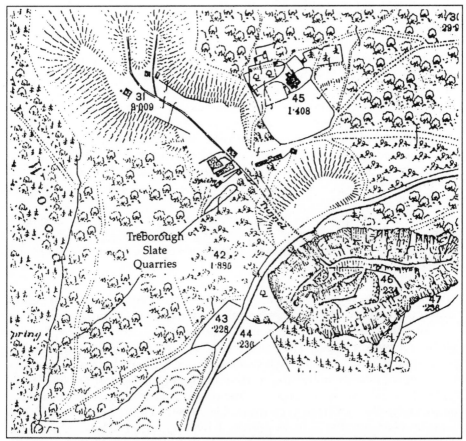

O.S. County Series 25in. Smo. XLVII 15 of 1888. By 1903 a further quarry had been opened up to the north of the road and south-west of the works. The quarry shown here has now been completely filled in by refuse.

the Trevelyan family of Nettlecombe Court to John Webber of Huish Champflower for a rental of £13 per annum. The 1841 Tithe Map shows a quarry of over two acres in extent being worked by a William Southwood whilst in 1845 it was being worked by the well known Cornish mining engineer, Nicholas Ennor.

In 1850, a William Pritchard of Caernarvon, with two fellow Welshmen, leased the quarry and began vigorously expanding the workings. By 1858, with Pritchard now sole lessee, the workings had reached such a depth that a tunnel was driven from the quarry to the mill on the other side of the road. Annual production in 1858 amounted to 600 tons. After the death of William Pritchard in 1882, the quarry was managed by his widow Eleanor until closure in 1889. In 1893, Page referred to Treborough as being 'quite recently abandoned, much to the sorrow of the neighbourhood, as they afforded employment to a large number of men'.

In 1894 the Trevelyans decided to work the quarry on their own account and appointed a Thomas Voss as manager. After a few years spent in clearing out the old workings, slate production recommenced with output peaking in 1904-5 at 1000 tons. Overall, however, the workings did not repay with a loss being recorded in most years and in 1910 the quarry once again closed. The final phase of working ran from 1910 to 1935 when the Vickery family from Roadwater leased the quarry. A stationary steam engine was installed to solve the regularly occurring water problems, but a combination of antiquated machinery, under-capitalisation and competition finally forced closure in 1935.

By 1939 all slate quarrying in Somerset had come to an end. Inferior quality slate, poor transport, and primitive and dangerous working methods had all taken their toll. It was simply cheaper to bring in superior slate from other parts of the country.

At Treborough, much evidence can still be seen of the quarry working. In addition to the filled-in main quarry itself and the huge waste tips, there remain buildings, the tunnel, the still traceable wheelpit and its associated leat, and the remains of weighbridges. The slate occurs as a wide vein slanting into the ground and its extensive exploitation necessitated the eventual use of mechanical pumping and/or tunnelling to cope with the problems of the increasing depth of the pit. At Tracebridge and Treborough, these tunnels were used for haulage as well as drainage, with the mill being sited by the tunnel mouth. The slate was blasted out with black powder which continued to be used after the advent of dynamite in the 1870s because the latter tended to shatter the rock. Aerial ropeways were used to lift out the rock which was then manhandled on to a narrow-gauge tramway for transport to the mill. Here, the slate was cut into the required sizes by waterwheel-powered diamond-tipped circular saws. Roofing slates, however, had to be cut by hand, a highly skilled task which took several years to learn. It is believed that there were extensive underground workings at Treborough but access was blocked off years ago.

Some local buildings still carry roofs of Treborough slate, whilst in Treborough churchyard are the graves of William Pritchard and some of his employees, including one Isaac Chedzoy who 'met his death by an accident at the slate quarry in this parish, December 8th 1875 aged 45 years'. The dressing and tips area is accessible but the woods in which they lie are now a local nature reserve and visitors should respect this when examining the site.

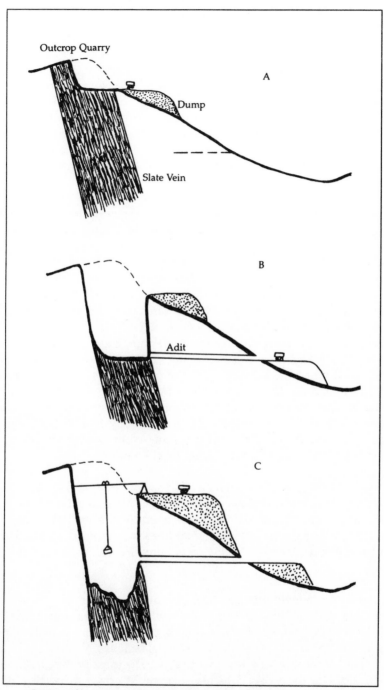

*Stages of extraction from the slate vein at Treborough quarry.
(Drawn by M.J. Messenger).*

107

The Lime Industry

Lime, or calcium oxide, has been used for building purposes since Roman times but during the Middle Ages its value as a fertiliser was appreciated, especially on newly-broken soils. By the late eighteenth century, it had become a product of considerable importance, as new methods of agriculture were introduced and the use of lime as a fertiliser was strongly recommended by the agriculturalists of the time. It was particularly valuable for improving acid soils such as those found on Exmoor and its surrounding uplands. It was in this period that the limestone quarries at Combe Martin, Exford and Nethercott were at the peak of their production.

Due to the high cost of transportation, landowners in the Exmoor area searched for suitable stone and small farm and estate kilns are scattered across the area, particularly on the southern boundary. However, stone suitable for burning was very scarce and large quantities of limestone, and the culm with which to burn it, were shipped over from South Wales, especially from the Gower peninsula. The draw-holes of the banks of kilns which were built alongside the quays at Lynmouth, Porlock and Minehead can still be seen. Where there were no harbour facilities, kilns were built on the shore just above the tide line, as at Heddon's Mouth, Worthy, Lee Abbey and Bossington Beach. Here the boats would have had to be beached at high tide and their cargo of stone and culm unloaded when the tide was out. The pair of kilns at Bossington, with a ramp leading up from the beach to the kilns' mouths, are fine examples. An additional incentive to use Welsh limestone was that the imported dolomitic limestone required a lower temperature for burning than the local stone and therefore less fuel was needed, rendering the whole process including transportation from Wales cheaper than using local limestone.

However, although the Turnpike Act of 1829 stated that 'No toll was to be levied on any vehicle carrying or conveying on the same day lime to be used for manure,' lime burnt on the coast had still often to be transported many miles over poor roads and tracks, and great quantities were needed – 2.5 to 3 tons per acre in some circumstances – so any local supplies within Exmoor itself were welcome.

Fortunately, there were thin bands of 'Roadwater Limestone' to be found in the slates and shales of the Ilfracombe Beds which crossed the area from north-west to south-east, and where these outcropped they were heavily exploited. Writing in the 1880s, W. H. Gamlin speaks of 'queues of carts and waggons which formed wherever lime was procurable'. The most prolific quarries were along the sides of the valley which is Combe Martin, for in the nineteenth century there were at least nine large pits being worked here and even at the beginning of this century four kilns were still in operation. However, transporting the lime to where it was most required was an expensive problem, for it was a long haul up out of Combe Martin. Outcrops of this 'Roadwater Limestone' occurred inland at Newland, Luckwell Bridge, Luxborough, Allercott, Nurcott and Treborough, and here the scale of these more conveniently sited workings can be seen. At Luckwell Bridge, the shallow 100ft (30m.) wide workings extend over half a mile, whilst the combined workings at Allercott and Nurcott (which were just over the hill from the long played-out Luxborough quarries) cover an area some ²/₃ mile (1000m.) long and 250yd (225m.) wide, four kilns being in operation here as early as 1808. The quarry at Nurcott (which did not close until the 1920s) was the deepest, requiring an incline on which to draw up the trucks of stone, worked by a waterwheel, the wheelpit for which can be seen beside the existing kiln facing the lane. There is a large kiln standing beside the road at Treborough but to what extent lime was burnt in this locality is not clear, for the huge quarries which were here were primarily for the extraction of slate.

By far the most impressive remains are those at Newland, near Exford, in the heart of the moor. Here, there were five kilns, served by two deep pits – both now flooded – the one to the east being the largest and about 100ft (30m.) deep. It had an incline with drum, and a pump, housed in a deep shaft at the top of the pit, with both incline and pump worked by a waterwheel some 250ft (75m.) away. The pump, 46ft (14m.) down the shaft, was coupled to a T-bob connected by flat rods to a crank on the 25ft (7.5m.) diameter waterwheel. The wheel was below ground level and was fed, via a tunnel, from a leat off Pennycombe Water, with both the tail water and drainage water from the pit being taken away in tunnels back to the stream. The T-bob house, two of the larger kilns and many other features survive. With Combe Martin, these pits provided most of the lime required by John and Frederic Knight for their improvement of Exmoor.

To the south of the region, there were limekilns around South Molton, with the Throckmorton estate having their own near Molland. There were a few other small kilns scattered around, using inferior stone, but they contributed little to the general need.

When the West Somerset Mineral Railway gave easy access to the Brendon Hills, limestone from the Watchet area, as well as culm from South Wales, could be carried up and a fine pair of kilns survive near the line's junction with the branch to Raleighs Cross mine. High on Exmoor itself, where the proposed Simonsbath-Porlock railway was to cross Colonel Blathwayt's estate, provision of land was made to build limekilns although, like the railway, this dream was never realised.

The actual kilns used developed over time. The Romans used substantial limekilns, which were described by Cato (234-149 BC) but there is no evidence of them using lime during their occupation of the North Devon/Somerset coast. The earliest agricultural 'kilns' were little more than limepits in which coal and limestone were piled in layers until a heap was made which protruded above the lip. This was then covered by turves, fired and left to burn slowly for a week or two. Medieval limekilns varied from a circular 4ft (1.2m.) high wall with two opposed stoke holes through to a circular wall about 10ft (3m.) in diameter and about 6ft (1.8m.) in height with draught tunnels at the base. A brushwood fire would be overlaid by both limestone and coal in alternate layers until a heap was formed and this again would be covered by turves. This type of kiln was known as a flare kiln and was allowed to burn out before emptying. By the end of the eighteenth century, running perpetual or draw kilns had become more popular and the bottle kiln was introduced. This was a large stone or brick-built bowl about 10ft (3m.) in diameter, parallel-sided for several feet and then tapering downwards to the bottom, rather like an inverted milk bottle. There is a grate at the bottom for drawing out the lime, reached by a short arched tunnel and this was usually set into the slope of a hillside so that the top of the kiln was at the level of the adjoining quarry floor, which provided for ease of loading, but did lead at times to accidents where limeburners and persons sheltering fell in. Coal was brought to the same level and when the kiln was burning the stone and coal were fed in alternately, and lime and ashes drawn out at the bottom, so that the kiln worked continuously for weeks on end. Cement kilns were like the traditional limekilns, except that the openings were kept as small as possible to conserve heat and they were fired on an intermittent rather than continuous basis.

In discussing the lime industry, mention should be made of the use of lime for the production of mortar and plaster as well as cement. Until the invention of Portland cement in 1824, lime mortars were the principal cementing agent in building. These were produced by mixing sand with slaked lime (calcium hydroxide) or hydrated lime. The lime cement produced in the Watchet area was especially prized. While building the Eddystone Lighthouse in 1757-9, Smeaton specified that Watchet lime be used, having it transported to Plymouth by packhorse. Earlier, in 1724, Defoe noted that the lime cement produced from the stone quarried from the cliffs around the Watchet area was especially longlasting and suitable for the construction of heads, piers and other masonry that was to lie underwater.

This did not go unnoticed as the Luttrells of Dunster Castle, who held the manor of Old Cleeve, utilised the liassic limestone for lime and cement and the gypsum for the production of plaster of Paris. The massive form of gypsum, known as alabaster, has been used for carving ornaments, at first religious figures and then later for tourists. This use of the gypsum continued into the twentieth century, with Whittaker and Green (1984) describing how it was dug from the cliffs and then taken by boat and cart to Watchet. Working is thought to have ceased by 1923.

The main production of cement, however, took place at Washford in a former fulling mill. In 1885, Messrs Symons, Frean & Company of the Washford Bow Mill are mentioned in an advertisement and later, using the title of Warren Cement Works, sold hydraulic, Portland and rendering cements.

Building and Roadstone Quarries

Disused quarries and pits mark the many places where stone has been dug for local use in roads and buildings, with poor quality local material commonly having been used in preference to better stone from some distance away. On the northern slopes of Rowley Down at Lawns quarry, which is now an overgrown rubbish tip, a thin sandstone was extracted within the Combe Martin slates; sandstones were also dug in the Kentisbury slates at Great Gate quarry (SS 613425) and at numerous small workings on the high ground at Kentisbury Down, Rowley Down, Challacombe Common, North Regis Common, Broadmead, Goat Hill, Great Ashcombe and Little Ashcombe.

The Morte slates have been worked for building stone such as at Wallover Down and Castle quarries (SS 705388) and a series of quarries on the South Molton to Simonsbath road, both for building and for the production of roadstone.

The main roadstone quarries at present are situated in the Bray valley and are operated by Archibald Nott & Sons and by Devon County Council. These quarries started to expand to their present size just after the First World War when there was a demand for roadstone for use in conjunction with tar, to produce a waterproof seal. This started to appear in the second half of the nineteenth century and followed on from the work of Telford and Macadam, who totally changed the methods of road construction by using varying sizes of stone and dust in order to provide a hard surface.

In the early twentieth century, it was common for light railways to be constructed along roads in order to transport stone from the quarries which were specially opened if no other quarry existed along the route. This involved the use of 2ft gauge steam locomotives and it is recorded that several were stored at the Beacon Down quarry in the early half of this century. From enquiries made, it would appear that although there was a tramway system in operation in this quarry, the locomotives were not used to pull the trams, this being done either by horse or by hand.

111

Acknowledgement

The authors are grateful to Derrick Warren for additional material on the lime industry.

MISCELLANEOUS INDUSTRIES

Derrick Warren

Most of the small 'industries' that existed in the little towns and villages that surround Exmoor depended either upon the products of agriculture or served its needs – wool, tanning, lime, agricultural implements etc. Some developed because the upland area gave a plentiful supply of water for power, a few from the entrepreneurial activities of landowners, whilst others grew from the craftsmen (tanners, blacksmiths, wheelwrights etc.) upon whom the largely self-sufficient settlements once depended for anything that needed to be made. These 'industries' were, even by contemporary standards, on a very small scale and most had ceased working by the end of the Second World War, but they were, in many ways, a rural microcosm of the more industrialised parts of Britain.

Agricultural Machinery Makers and Machinists

For centuries, local craftsmen had made the simple implements and tools that the farmer might require, but in the nineteenth century, with the mechanisation of many farming practices, it was the country implement maker and machinist who initially made the new machinery. They were clever men for not only had they to be blacksmith, wheelwright and carpenter, but also designer, book-keeper and salesman. Often they were innovators, even inventors, but it must be said that they were good copyists of the implements they had seen at shows or read about in journals. Where they differed fundamentally from the town agricultural machinery maker was that they had no facilities for casting their own ironwork and, although they made their own wood patterns, this work had to be contracted out to a nearby jobbing foundry. This was also a factor in the greater amount of wood employed in the making of many of their machines. They flourished nationally in the nineteenth century and the area around Exmoor was no exception.

John Brayley was the son of a South Molton tin smith and brazier and in the 1850s was a 'machine maker' in East Street, South Molton, employing ten men and boys, paying them wages of between £1 and 7/- per week. When his father-in-law's corn mill and farm at Wade, near Molland, fell vacant in 1861 he moved his business of 'thrashing machine maker' there, building a smithy and machine shop adjacent to the mill. He was a true entrepreneur for, besides being a machinist, he was also miller, farmer, carter and sawyer for the Throckmorton estate, of which he was a tenant. Between 1877 and 1893, when the iron mines at Molland closed, he helped haul out nearly 12,000 tons of ore down to Bishop's Nympton station, carting back timber from the Throckmorton woods.

When the Devon and Somerset Railway was being built in 1871-2, he was contractor to the company for the repair of tools, but his real work was as a machinist, making not only thrashing machines, but winnowers, hay machines, ploughs and cultivators. He also carried out repairs and installed new machinery for corn mills – he built and put in a new wheel at Lower Mill, Exford, in 1870 at a cost of £40 – as well as building and installing waterwheels, with their ancillary shafting, pulleys etc. at many farms. Although his writing and spelling were poor, with figures and practical engineering it was another matter, for in 1867 he drew up detailed specifications for a new water-powered sawmill for an estate at Stoodleigh, near Tiverton. This included a 30ft by 5ft (9.1 by 1.5m.) waterwheel, gearing, rack-saw and line shafting with drums (pulley wheels) for other machines. The estimate for all this, including erection and good running for a year, was £450 – a very large sum indeed in those days and an indication of the capabilities of a machinist. On his death in 1891 his second son, James, took over the business but he soon became only an agent for national machinery makers. His first son, John, became a mine captain at Molland and elsewhere although in 1906, at Withypool, he was described as 'machinist'. The mill, machine shop and other buildings still stand at Wade (SS 971266) and it is appropriate that the site has recently been taken over as a timber yard.

All across the West Country, there are still to be found working (albeit converted to tractor use) the ploughs and hay rakes made by John Huxtable of West Buckland. John and Richard Huxtable were blacksmith and wheelwright respectively at Brayford in 1850, John moving later to a large workshop at West Buckland. There the story would stop – the building itself is now cottages – were it not for a detailed contemporary description of the works as in 1889, and what was made there. Descriptions of individual works of that time are rare, and for a small country works such as this even rarer. At one end of the building was an 18ft (5.5m.) waterwheel, built by Garnish & Lemon of Barnstaple, which, by a shaft running the length of the building, worked the machines – a large grindstone, a self-acting drilling machine, adapted by John Huxtable as a multiple three-hole drill to drill the holes in the cross-pieces of his expanding rakes, and a self-acting lathe, with milling cutters attached to its mandrel to cut the rack gear of the sliding bars of the rakes, again adapted by Huxtable. There were three forges for his blacksmiths, a gauge block used as a standard in making the ploughshares and patent tool to make the square links for the harrows, both these to Huxtable's design. All the machines manufactured were made entirely of malleable iron including a patent reversible plough, a patent plough which could be converted into a digger to break up furrows, a patent adjustable and replaceable coulter, chain harrows and his famous expanding hay rake, the teeth of which could be regulated, by means of a 'lazy-tongs' action, for different types of work. The works was moved to Barnstaple in 1896.

In the 1860s, Henry Quick had a smithy and small workshop off Lady Street,

Dulverton, and was 'wheelwright, builder, spring trap manufacturer, agricultural implement and machine maker, agent for all the principal manufacturers of reaping and mowing machines and dog cart builder'. Robert Page took over the business in 1882 and greatly extended the premises, with a long workshop parallel to Lady Street, over which was an assembly shop and a paint shop. The machines were subsequently powered by a Pool oil engine. Page became an 'agricultural implement manufacturer, mechanical engineer, wheelwright and blacksmith' and later simply 'machinist and coachbuilder'. He made small thrashing machines, reed makers, saw benches and constructed waterwheels, one of which is still working one of his in-barn thrashing machines. He moved with the times, becoming an agent for farm machinery but when one of his sons joined him, he concentrated on being a coachbuilder, making high quality gigs, traps and governesses carts etc., much sought after at sales today. The buildings survived intact until the late 1980s when the site was developed.

Thomas Phillips and his three sons were, in 1851, all wheelwrights and carpenters at Bridgetown, Exton. One son, James, went on to be miller and auctioneer and another, Charles, to found the 'Exe Valley Wheel Works' where he was 'millwright, machinist, agricultural implement maker and agent, wheelwright and carpenter'. He made sawbenches (using oak for the framework), harrows, a 'very serviceable' combined seed and corn drill and light in-barn thrashers. In 1909, he moved to the old corn/sawmill at Cowbridge near Timberscombe, and was there joined by his son Henry who had been apprenticed to Rustons of Lincoln and who had had his own premises in Friday Street, Minehead. Henry was making and installing waterwheels on farms as late as 1930 and two of his in-barn thrashers are still at work on Exmoor today. He died in 1936, his father surviving him by several years. The premises at Cowbridge (SS 956425) are now occupied by S. Grabham & Sons, gate and fence manufacturers, Sam Grabham having joined Henry as an employee in 1911, staying with the firm until it closed.

The firm of W.H. Pool & Sons of Chipstable was unusual on several counts – started in 1845 it survived until 1956; both sons were the equal to their father (one being an extremely clever engineer and innovator); and one of their products was, for a time, unique in the West Country. W.H. Pool was trained as a wheelwright in Bristol and although he always made long-carts and wagons, by 1847 he was making simple, hand-fed in-barn thrashing machines (similar in design to those of Ferrabee in 1843), horse gearing, a patented American hay collector, drag rakes, apple crushers and cider presses (one, made in 1851, is in use now). The ironwork required was made by his father-in-law, Samuel Surridge, the smith at Waterrow (whose son, James, later became a well known edge-tool maker). Pool was also a farmer while his wife, Emma, kept the village shop, carried on by their daughter, Maria. When W.H. Pool was joined by his sons, William and Alfred, the business expanded, having its own smithy, brass foundry etc. and producing corn and seed drills, sheep shearers, rack and saw benches and sophisticated single and double blast in-barn thrashers. The cast iron work for all these was made by foundries at Exeter, Wellington and Tiverton. This expansion was made possible by powering the works by an oil engine, designed and patented by Alfred in 1891. Although the castings were done by Easton's of Taunton, these engines were made entirely at Chipstable (the crank-shafts being forged by hand) and had a wide sale to farms and small works throughout the West. It was only the introduction of small, fast, petrol engines from America during the First World War that ensured their demise and the gradual run-down of the firm. They never employed many hands (14 at most) but their products must have had a profound effect on the rural economy. The engines are now collectors' pieces whilst the last thrasher to be made – completed by employees after Alfred's death in 1956 – is now in the Somerset Rural Life Museum at Glastonbury together with one of their engines. Unhappily, the works were levelled and most records destroyed in 1956.

Of all the above implement makers at least something survives, but of Bartholomew Somerville of Parracombe all we know is that he was a 'mechanic' and 'machinist' from 1850 to 1857, whilst the only record of G.R.Turner of Combe Sydenham is that at the Bath and West Show in 1852 he exhibited two ploughs and a Patent Combined Reaping and Mowing Machine for Grass and Corn, priced £20 'the whole invented and made by the exhibitor'.

Millwrights

As has been seen, most machinists could make and install waterwheels, gearing etc., especially for farm use, but there were far fewer specialist millwrights capable of erecting and fully servicing wheels and ancillary machinery used to power the many works and corn mills. John Chidgey of Watchet was such a millwright. He had been apprenticed to his brother-in-law, the engineer for the Watchet paper works, to learn his trade of machinist and millwright and in 1856 he set up his own business in Watchet at Mount Pleasant. Initially, he was mainly concerned with the making of iron- and brasswork needed by the shipping which visited the port but soon concentrated his activities on millwrighting. By the 1870s, he was employing four men and his premises had become too small so, in 1880, he took over an old blacksmith's shop in South Road, where he built a small brass foundry, pattern maker's shop and a machine shop where lathes, drills and a shaper and planer (c.1860 – secondhand) were installed, powered by a water motor, an improved version of which he patented in 1894. This motor was worked off the 1in. high pressure mains. By this time, he had been joined by his two sons, William and Henry, and the business flourished, doing work as far away as Cheddar, across the channel in South Wales and down in Devon. The firm was responsible for all the work for the large roller mills of Stoate & Sons in Watchet and in the early 1900s was producing prefab-ricated milling plants. The workforce had increased to 14, including a full-time stonedresser. John died in 1915 when already the use of water power was declining and his sons did not diversify.

The firm closed in 1936, although the premises continued to be used by John's nephew-in-law as an automobile repair shop and during the Second World War the machine shop produced munitions. In 1976, all the machines, tools and wooden patterns were given to the Somerset Museum Service and are stored, pending future re-erection. By far the most interesting acquisition were five day-books of the firm, from which it has been possible to trace, price and, in many cases, see examples of the firm's work which survive. A fine example is an undershot waterwheel at Bridge Farm, Williton. Erected for the Wyndham estate in 1890, the cost for the 11ft by 3ft 4in. (3.3 by 1m.) wheel was £61.10s. and £13.15s.11 ¹/₂d. for the screens, hatches, bearings etc. The firm also made two new wooden waterwheels for the mill at Dunster but why the Luttrell estate stipulated the use of wood is not recorded. The only other specialist millwright in the whole of West Somerset and North Devon was the firm of Garnish & Lemon of Barnstaple.

Ironfounders

Nothing is known about the first owners of the Watchet Foundry in Swain Street nor what they made. Lacey & Company were iron and brass founders there in 1852 but had closed in 1856, and W.H. Hole then took over the firm fol-lowed by his son, Charles. About 1890, it was acquired by the Williton agricul-tural engineering firm of J. Gliddon & Sons who worked it until 1948, making a wide range of domestic and agricultural ironwork including kitchen ranges, hot water systems, waterpumps and, in the early days, the ubiquitous water-wheel. They also undertook heavy castings for the West Somerset branch of the Great Western Railway and for the Lynton and Lynmouth Cliff Railway. The works employed between 18 and 30 men, depending upon work, and had a 18ft (5.5m.) furnace, the fan providing the blast being powered by a gas engine which, when not so occupied, powered the lathes and other machines. There was another iron founder, Walter Lane, in Water Street, Dunster, but how long he worked or what he made is not recorded.

Wheelwrights

Craft trades such as that of wheelwright and carpenter are generally outside the scope of this book, but some grew to such an extent that their trade became much more than local. Two carpenter/wheelwrights come to mind – Jones of

Lynn Mill and William Floyd of Oaklands, Brendon. Although their premises had long been derelict when seen in 1974, the surviving lay shafting and pulley wheels for their machines showed the extent of their operations as did their power units – a 14in. horizontally-shafted Francis turbine working under a 16ft head (off an extension to the trough to the overshot waterwheel of the old Lynn Mill) and a 21ft by 3ft 6in. (6.4 by 1.1m.) waterwheel built by Floyd himself in 1870. Floyd was a wheelwright, coffin maker and general carpenter whose business survived right up to the floods of 1952 when the buildings and launder to the waterwheel were damaged. John How, however, was a wheelwright of an entirely different calibre. Some time in the 1840s, he set up his business in the tiny Brendon Hills village of Kings Brompton and by the 1870s was employing 17 men – carpenters, wheelwrights, blacksmiths and sawyers – making a wide range of wagons and carts for which the firm became famous over a wide area. A sample of those made during the period 1873-4 together with their prices gives some indication of the scope of his enterprise:

1873	April 24	New cart	£ 7. 10. 0.
	26	New barrow	10. 6.
	June 16	New two-horse wagon	12. 5. 0.
	Sept 9	Two new currys [a light two-wheeled cart for hay and corn]	12. 0. 0.
	19	New timber carriage	16. 10. 0.
	29	New broad-wheeled cart (putt)	5. 10. 0.
	Nov 16	New two-wheeled timber carriage	9. 10. 0.
		Extra for broad wheels	12. 0.
1874	Feb 11	New one-horse cart	3. 10. 0.
	April 28	New wagon	13. 10. 0.

How felled, hauled out and cut all his own timber, some being seasoned for as long as twelve years. He had his own livery for his wagons: the iron-work was silver or red and blue with white or yellow striping; nuts and bolts were black; the inside of carts was red and the outside blue; shafts and axles were red with the wheels red with white or yellow striping. At this period every operation was done with hand tools.

With the coming of the Devon and Somerset Railway to Dulverton in 1872, his business expanded dramatically, with eventually two wagons a week being sent to agents in Oxford, Banbury and Basingstoke. Some, such as wagons for transporting cattle and larger putts for use on lowland pastures, were especially made for this trade. His wagons were exhibited at the Royal Show (not by himself but by his agents who, it is sadly reported, then charged double the prices paid to him!). By this time he had been joined by his son, Joseph, and in the 1890s they built a new brick machine and carpenter's shop. On the ground floor were the rack, bench and band saws, planer and lathe, powered by a

Ruston Hornsby oil engine which also worked the blower for the hearths across the yard and later a generator for electric light. Above the machine shop was the carpenters shop where the wagons were made and assembled before being lowered to have their wheels fitted and then sent to the paintshop.

A trade was developed with South Wales, especially with dairies for light milk floats, and the extent of this trade can be judged by the fact that it was here that a bad debt was incurred of £500 which, however, the firm was strong enough to ride. There was a contract with Metal Agency of Bristol (later UBM) for making all their wheel-barrows. Joseph, in his turn, was joined by his three sons – Ronald, John and Ernest – and the firm continued to prosper, eventually employing 25 men. However, the tractor gradually superseded the horse and the last vehicle, a putt, was built in the late 1940s. The firm then relied on the repair of wagons and building and carpentry work until it closed in 1985. The premises were redeveloped in 1991 but all the machines and tools had been acquired by the Somerset Rural Life Museum at Glastonbury.

When he started, John How did not confine himself to wheelwrighting for, with his uncle Thomas (a master mason) he also became a builder of some repute. In 1864, they rebuilt Bryant's Bridge for the Dulverton Highways Board and four years later they built a new bridge for the Board at Pulham's Mill for £17. 10s. Their own parish church of St Mary was restored and refurnished by them in 1853, but their lasting memorial must surely be St Luke's Church at Simonsbath. When Exmoor became a civil and ecclesiastical parish in 1856, it was John How's firm which built and furnished its church for the sum of £ 2972. 6s. As this sum also included the cost of the rectory it is presumed that they built it also.

Bricks, Tiles and Pottery

With Bridgwater and its long-established reputation for the manufacture of bricks and tiles only a few miles along the coast, it seems surprising that bricks, tiles and pottery should have been made commercially around Minehead as well as for local and estate use, yet their production commenced in the 1750s and lasted nearly 200 years.

A John Mogg, of Bristol, was appointed to set up and work a brickyard for the Luttrell estate of Dunster at the Warren, on the coast to the east of Minehead, in 1759. The estate accounts of that time record '2 days work for himself and his wife in Sorting, Chipping and Stoping Cracks and packing away each kiln of Goods at 2s. 3d. per day for 14 days'. At the beginning, coarse kitchen ware was made as well as bricks and, by the end of the century, plain tiles, pantiles, ridge tiles and bars for the kilns of malthouses were also being produced. It was a very small operation for in 1786 only 9320 bricks were made and out of those 1550 were for estate use. Even so, prices had to be kept down because of the competition from Bridgwater. The yard had the title of Brick and Tile Works but in 1819 it only comprised 'one Yard containing one Workhouse, one Shed, four Hacks (stacks of bricks in rows waiting firing) and one Kiln'. At the end of the nineteenth century, it was managed by Samuel Cornish and the range of products was increased to include clay field drain pipes. It closed in 1919 and the site now lies below the Somerwest holiday complex.

In 1860, another small brick kiln was in operation at Blue Anchor, worked by Robert Henson who was also the proprietor of the Blue Anchor Hotel and Family Boarding House. The kiln survives (ST 028433) and is listed Grade II.

Brickmaking was only one of John Ridler's enterprises. He operated brick and tile works at Porlock Weir between 1840 and 1888, many of his bricks being sold to Bolitho & Sons of Penzance to be used as ballast for his cargoes of oak bark.

There is reference to a tile and pottery kiln in Pool's Wood, Bossington, working at the end of the eighteenth century. It was operated by the manor of Doverhay but it is doubtful whether it was on any sort of commercial basis.

The only small yard not in this area was at Morebath, worked by J.Besley during the 1850s, using a white clay deposited on the slate.

The Victoria Brick and Tile Works at Alcombe, near Minehead, was however entirely different. Established in 1897 by John B. Marley, it eventually covered 10 acres, had tramways to bring the clay from the pits to the works, two tall chimney stacks taking away the smoke from the oval Hoffman kilns and at its peak was producing 60,000 bricks per week. Its product went to Ireland, Cornwall and along the south coast. It continued working until 1947 when the demand for clay bricks declined. The site is now a housing estate and a fire station.

The kiln of a tiny pottery, started by the Luttrell estate in the Deer Park at Dunster at the same time as their brickyard, still survives (SS 993438). It was worked at first by the same John Mogg who ran the Warren brickyard but after his death in 1760 it was worked by a succession of potters, one being James Norris who came from Crock Street, where the locally famous Donyatt pottery was made. A wide range of domestic ware was made including platters, pitchers, pans, washing bowls and pans for commodes, and the period up to 1770 was recorded as being successful. The potters did not hire the kiln but were paid for their skill and labour and this included the provision of lodgings and a generous liquor allowance – firing a kiln was thirsty work! The following advertisement appeared in the *Western Flying Post* of 5 February 1759, so the business must still have been thriving:

Wanted, At a New Yard set up near Minehead in Somerset, A Person that understands making and burning (with Welch Coals) Bricks, Tyles, and other Goods, and can undertake the whole Management of a Brick and Tyle Yard. Also a good Hand for making Panty'e. And also is wanted, a Person that can undertake making and burning of all sorts of Coarse Pottery Ware. Any sober Person, well qualified for either of the said business, and who can produce a good Character, shall have confident Employ, and great Encouragement – Application may be made to George Gale, at Dunster in the said County.

It is not known when the kiln closed. Although the kiln is in the garden of the Luttrell Arms Hotel, it can be viewed over the fence from the grounds of the Castle.

Tanning

As late as the nineteenth century, most villages had their bootmaker and many also had a tanner to supply him with leather. Tanners are recorded at Dulverton, Dunster, North Molton, Parracombe, Washford and Watchet. Some businesses were more than just a craftsman working on his own – at Washford, John Wood and his son were fellmongers as well as tanners and had a 'skin yard'; the tannery at Alcombe was large enough to have its own barkmill; whilst at Watchet the small tannery building, with its wooden louvred openings, can still be seen in Anchor Street. Many house names recall their previous use or the occupation of former inhabitants – Tanyard Farm, Tanners Cottage, with a Tan House at Treborough. At Heasley Mill, evidence of old tan pits and the watercourses that fed them, was recently uncovered.

In Minehead, the Siderfin family commenced tanning in 1794 on a site between the Avenue and Summerland Avenue, now occupied by the Regal cinema (of course this was well on the outskirts of the town at that date and must have been a cause of complaint by later holiday visitors!). By the time the firm was taken over by W.L. Evans in 1894 (while still retaining the name John Siderfin & Company until it closed in the 1920s), it was a large and prosperous concern with two boilers, each with its own tall chimney stack, to provide the hot water for the processing and power to turn the drums and paddles. It produced butts and sole leather made largely from hides imported from South America through the port of Watchet. The buildings were demolished when the Regal was built in 1934.

Porlock had a long history of tanning, probably due to its proximity to the oak woods which still clothe the slopes of the nearby combes. An 'Assize of Leather' was held in the town in the thirteenth century and in 1607 a lawsuit is recorded over water rights between Walter Stocke, tanner and Robert Dyer, yeoman. In the 1890s, when stables were being built at Whitehall, in Hawkcombe, ancient elm-lined tan pits were uncovered, still containing a quantity of yellowish clay – the fullers earth which was used to help remove grease from the hides (this was obtained from around Bath and Crewkerne).

However, the area which had the longest history of tanning in Porlock, and the site of the dispute between Stocke and Dyer, is Sparkhayes, just north of the High Street. In 1840, the tanyard there was rented from the Blathwayt estate by Mary Rawle. In 1852, George Rawle was the tanner and Mary the currier, and by 1869 George had been joined by his son, John, with Mary still currier. In 1880 Tom Pearce who, with his brother, had a tannery at South Molton, came into the firm and it became Rawle and Pearce. Up to that time, it had been a very small concern employing only one man but Pearce must have injected capital into the business. By 1897, it had become Thomas Pearce, Tanners, and when his sons joined him, Thomas Pearce & Sons; it so remained until it closed in 1939. Extensive buildings had been put up, a 14ft by 4ft (4.3 by 1.2m.) waterwheel installed, and a small office built at the entrance to the High Street to clock in the 30 to 40 men eventually employed there.

When the Wheelhouse was no longer needed to help provide the town with electricity, it was acquired by the Pearces to light the works. During the nineteenth century, oak bark was exported from Porlock Weir by John, and later Thomas, Ridler (they had a wooden 'bark house' on the beach there for storing it). However, by 1900, the Porlock Tannery took all the bark that could be produced locally and had to buy in quantities from other sources. During the Second World War, the buildings were used as billets for troops and subsequently became the site of the Exmoor Engineering Company. Although the tan pits are now filled in and form a car park and gardens, the buildings are being converted into craft workshops, flats etc., with the character and look of a tannery being retained. The yard is accessible to the public.

Chemicals

In the 1860s, Thomas Lomas moved his chemical manure business from Middlesbrough, Yorkshire to Minehead where he set up the Bristol Channel Chemical, Sulphuric Acid and Chemical Manure Works. One factory, manufacturing sulphuric acid, glue and chemical manure, was on West Quay beyond the gasworks; another producing charcoal by 'the destructive distillation of wood in the absence of air' with acetic acid, methanol (wood alcohol), acetone and fusel oil as by-products was at Warren Point; and a similar works was near Kings Brompton.

In 1872, he sold the West Quay works to a Mr Hellier (this burned down in

1887), tried to dispose of the Warren Point site and in 1874 sold his 'Wood Works' at Kings Brompton to the Wolverhampton firm of Bayliss, Jones & Bayliss, manufacturers of wrought iron gates, railings, tree guards etc. They formed, with Lucas, 'The West of England Iron, Wood & Charcoal Company' and moved the operations to Pool, near Exebridge where it became, as well as a chemical works, a timber yard and a depot for the products of the Wolverhampton firm. Charcoal continued to be produced there until 1914 but it became increasingly a sawmill.

Timber and Sawmills

The Forest of Exmoor is somewhat of a misnomer for it had been bare of trees for a very long time when John Knight took it over in 1818. In fact, a survey by the Commissioners of Woods and Forests in 1814 recorded only 37 trees within the area of the Forest, and all of those were around Simonsbath House. John Knight appreciated what value shelter belts and woods would give, but by 1840 only 25 acres (Birch Cleave) had been planted. Thereafter, more progress was made and by 1850 the appearance of parts of the moor was changing drastically, and soon a sawmill was needed. This was built in the 1860s by Frederic Knight at Simonsbath and had a large waterwheel of approximately 30ft (9.1m.) in diameter, taking its water from two sources: a pond north of the Challacombe road, fed by a leat off Ashcombe Water, and directly from Bale Water via a half-mile-long leat. The sawmill machinery consisted of a locally built rack saw and a table sawbench made by Sam Worssam, Oakley Works, Chelsea, London (both still in situ). In about 1897, after Knight had sold the reversion of the Forest in 1886 to the Fortescue Estate, the waterwheel was replaced by a turbine made by H.P. Vacher, of Winchester (also in situ). This took its water, in a new leat, directly from the River Barle. When the weir and leat were washed out by the floods of 1952 this turbine was itself replaced by a 40h.p. Ruston Hornsby oil engine. The whole complex has now been acquired by the Exmoor National Park to continue in use as a sawmill using the original machinery.

The woodlands in the valleys surrounding the moor had, however, been managed for centuries, both for standing timber and for coppicing. Coppiced trees were used to provide the oak bark for the tanners and for charcoal burning. The oak bark used for tanning had to be stripped from the trees under twenty years old in the spring and then dried, sometimes in the open, but more often in bark houses where it was then stored. By the late nineteenth and early twentieth centuries the local tanneries were taking large quantities of bark, but 200 years before then bark was a very important product – during the first half of the eighteenth century oak bark was the major export, along with grain, from the port of Minehead.

Although there is little direct evidence of charcoal burning, charcoal must once have been in great demand by the bloomeries and for copper and silver-lead smelting. Most of these woods belonged to the large estates so, when technology moved beyond the sawpit, they set up their own sawmills, both to provide timber for their own estate use and as a cash crop. All were initially water powered – at Marsh Street, Dunster, for the Luttrells; at Holnicote for the Aclands (where a Vortex turbine, made by Stenner and Gunn of Loman Works, Tiverton, replaced the14ft (4.3m.) waterwheel); and on the Carnarvon estate at Pixton, near Dulverton. Here, a 22h.p. propellor turbine, made by Gilbert, Gilkes and Gordon of Kendal, under a 23ft (7m.) head, worked, with an oil-pressure governor, not only the sawbenches but an alternator to provide electricity. A purpose-built sawmill at Knowle, near Timberscombe, had a 16ft by 3ft (4.9 by 0.9m.) overshot waterwheel, and was fitted out by W. H. Pool and Sons of Chipstable, although in 1909 all the machinery was transferred to the old corn mill at Cowbridge. When the Throckmorton estate abandoned their sawpit at Abbots Cross, Molland, they converted the old Bottreaux corn mill. Perhaps the most unusual sawmill was that for the small estate at Woolhanger. Here the sawbenches were powered by a waterwheel (built by Floyd of Brendon) that was originally installed to work the bellows of an organ in the ornate octagonal music room attached to the house.

Eventually many small commercial sawmills were set up – at Watchet, Minehead, Combe Martin, Roadwater, Porlock and at West Knowle, near Brushford – the latter powered by a 14ft by 4ft (4.3 by 1.2m.) breastshot water-wheel supplemented at a later date by a Pool oil engine.

The largest sawmill in the area, and reputedly the largest in the West of England at one time, was the one at Pool (see Chemicals). In 1899, it reverted to being Bayliss, Jones & Bayliss with Samuel Marsh as manager. The yard had two steam engines to work the machinery, which included a very large horizontal reciprocating saw frame and two jib derricks, but later the larger of the two engines worked an alternator so that the works could be run by electricity. Samuel's son succeeded as manager when the firm became Bartlett & Bayliss in 1914 and remained until 1926. By then they were employing over 30 hands and operated a fleet of Foden tractors. It became Dulverton Sawmills in 1935 and remained in operation until the 1960s. Throughout its life, it had been contractor to the railway companies – particularly the Great Western Railway – for the supply of beech keys (wedges) and ferrelles (wooden washers) used in track-laying and for sleepers. They were also suppliers to the Admiralty of stem and stern posts for light naval vessels, which, during the Second World War, were used for magnetic mine sweeping.

Malthouses

The Vale of Porlock had long been famous for the growing of superb malting barley, so it is hardly surprising that Porlock should have had its own malthouse. Situated in Sparkhayes, it was run during the last century by, in turn, John Chibbet and Michael Ridler, and latterly by Richard G. Richards, with the last malting taking place in 1946. The buildings have now been developed.

Maltsters are recorded in most small communities – Watchet, Combe Martin, North Molton and even Luxborough. The little malthouse still surviving at Lynch (SS 900476), between Bossington and Allerford, shows very clearly on what an extremely small scale all these undertakings would have been. In 1852 this malthouse was worked, in conjunction with Lynch Mill, by John Clarke, who also had interests in shipping, the lime workings at Newland and another mill at Horner. The malthouse can be seen clearly from the road.

Flour Mills

The size of Town Mills, Watchet (ST 070431), was an exception for corn mills in this area. In 1832, it was leased by Thomas Stoate from the Wyndham estate for £121 p.a. and became a very large mill indeed, with ten pairs of stones. Thomas Stoate was joined by his son, William, and in 1885 the mill was completely re-equipped with roller milling machinery, elevators etc. (installed by J. Chidgey & Sons) and steam power was introduced. In 1903, the waterwheel was replaced by a turbine. Roller mills required hard, dry grain and this was brought in through the harbour of Watchet and flour was sent to Ireland, South Wales and Bristol. In 1898, this trade was greatly disrupted when the harbour at Watchet was destroyed in the great storm, so the firm, now William Stoate & Sons, moved part of its business to Bristol and when, in 1911, the mill at Watchet was partially gutted by fire, the whole undertaking was transferred to that city. The remaining buildings were subsequently used for other purposes but have been threatened by re-development of the area.

Hydro-Electric Power Generation

With their scattered populations and poor communications, West Somerset and North Devon were not ideal areas for the provision of public utilities. Minehead had been supplied with town gas in 1868, with an extension main to Dunster in 1907, and the Watchet & Williton Coal and Gas Company was producing gas for Watchet in 1866, but gas was provided nowhere else. The area was, however, ideally suited for the production of electricity by water power and systems were set up in Lynmouth, Dulverton and Porlock.

The Victorians had 'taken up' Lynton and Lynmouth as a picturesque holiday resort which became known as the 'English Alps by the Sea', but although the well-to-do visitors could enjoy running water (courtesy of the Lynton Water Company Ltd) they must have wanted those other amenities to which they were accustomed – good street and domestic lighting. Thus, the provision of electric lighting must have appeared as an attractive proposition, particularly as it could be generated by water power.

So it was that in 1889 Mr Charles Geen founded the Devon Electric Light Company, and by March 1890 the generating station was in operation on the East Lyn River, making Lynmouth only the sixth town in the country to have a hydro-electric system. From a weir across the East Lyn, 400 yd (366m.) of open leat and 520 yd (475m.) of iron pipe gave a head of water of about 90ft (27m.) to a 'Little Giant' horizontally-shafted reaction turbine of 150h.p., made by Charles Louis Hett of Brigg, Lincolnshire. This was coupled to two Morley alternators, giving 37.5 kW at 2000V. The distribution was by underground cable with transformers to step down the current.

Demand soon exceeded supply and with the formation of a new company, the Lynton and Lynmouth Electric Lighting Company, additional turbines and alternators were installed. Because the East Lyn could not provide more water (in fact, its flow was steadily decreasing), a pumped storage system was set up which was probably the first in the world used in the generation of electricity. The supply to the town was only available between half an hour before sunset and midnight and in the winter from 6.30am to 9.00am so, at other times and when demand was low, the available water was pumped to a 190,000 gallon reservoir on the top of Summerhouse Hill (about 750ft (229m.) above the station) using a new separate turbine. When demand was high, a Pelton wheel on the same shafting used this water to supplement the power of the Little Giant. An additional low-pressure turbine was installed, also supplemented by a Pelton wheel, with another alternator.

The Lynmouth Central Station, from the Electrician, *August 1891.*

By 1899, 59 incandescent lamps of 32cp were lighting the streets with an arc lamp of 2000cp on the Rhenish Tower at the harbour mouth. The Local Board paid £3 per lamp and private customers either a flat rate per lamp or a unit charge of 8d. in summer and 5d. in winter for the first hour of the day and 4¹/₂d. thereafter. Two, more efficient Swiss inward-flow Escher Wyss turbines were subsequently installed and, later still, oil engines supplemented the supply to cope with greatly increased demand. Mr Geen remained as managing director until 1923 and the plant, including the two original Pelton wheels, was the sole supply for the area until destroyed by the flood of 1952, although at that time a connection to the National Grid was in the course of construction. Now only the concrete leat can be seen and traces of the reservoir on Summerhouse Hill.

Dulverton's supply is not so well documented. A Crompton 75V, 30 amp alternator was initially driven by a waterwheel on the town leat (Lower Mill?) and later by a Pool oil engine. This alternator still survives at Bridgetown where it was later worked by an 8ft (2.4m.) undershot waterwheel to light the mill. By 1906, the Dulverton Electric Lighting Company Ltd had been set up with Mr Barrow as Secretary. A concrete weir was built across the Barle between Dulverton and Brushford and two Armfield (of Ringwood, Hants) River Patent turbines, in an open flume setting with an approximate head of 8ft (2.4m.), were installed in a corrugated iron building over the river. These were later replaced by two Escher Wyss vertically-shafted turbines, each giving 50 kW with ample water. The company merged with the Exe Valley Electricity Company Ltd in 1930 (owned by the West of England Electricity Company, itself a subsidiary of Whitehall Securities) and the plant, now known as the Beasley Power Station, continued working until 1938 when the National Grid reached the area. It was, however, maintained as an emergency stand-by supply and was last used during the Second World War when German bombing disrupted supplies. It was dismantled in the 1950s but the weir, building and associated concrete work survives largely intact.

The supply for Porlock was extremely simple. When Hawkcombe Mill fell into disuse, it was bought in 1909 by the Porlock Electricity Company and the single-storied building had an additional storey added to house the batteries with a new 14ft by 3ft (4.3 by 0.9m.) overshot waterwheel, built by W. Huish of Porlock, and new gearing to work the alternator. At the same time in Porlock itself a new building, the Wheelhouse, was constructed on the site of the old Rectory Mill with a 15ft by 3ft6in. (4.6 by 1.1m.) overshot waterwheel built by Garnish and Lemon of Barnstaple, similar gearing to that at Hawkcombe, and a further bank of batteries. In total, the two plants produced 7 kW. By 1923, the demand recorded 19 kW but, by that time, other means of generating had been adopted and concentrated at Hawkcombe. A gas engine had been installed using producer gas manufactured on site and, later still, a diesel engine took over the work. By 1926, the station was supplying Luccombe, Selworthy,

Culbone and Oare but in 1932 the station closed, the supply being obtained from the Minehead Electric Supply Company (established about 1910). The bulk of the Porlock Company's capital had been acquired by Whitehall Securities in 1929 and they also controlled the Minehead Company.

Oddly enough, Porlock is the only town in the area still to have a generating station. Built in 1959, the stark, bunker-like station is situated behind the old tannery and provides an emergency supply for the area. It is powered by a Bristol Proteus gas-turbine engine (the industrial version of the power plant for the old Britannia airliner) capable of producing 2.7 megawatts, and it is owned by South West Power, a subsidiary of South Western Electricity.

The waterwheel and much of the gearing survives in the Wheelhouse (now called the Millhouse) whilst at Hawkcombe the wheel still turns, having been renovated in the early 1970s.

Where corn mills had replaced their waterwheels with turbines, these were sometimes later utilised to generate power, often for neighbouring houses as well as for themselves. In the parish of Old Cleeve, Collings Mill did just this, using a 10h.p. 15in. horizontally-shafted Armfield turbine and providing a few houses in Washford with their first electricity at 110V DC. Many farms and some private houses used water power before the power lines reached them in the 1960s. Chargot House at Luxborough is the first recorded example with plant being installed in 1890 by Edmundson's Electricity Corporation Ltd of London for the owner, J. H. Insole (a wealthy coalowner). The Francis-type horizontally-shafted turbine worked a generator producing 1.5 kW, 50/75V manufactured by the General Electricity Company, although this was possibly a replacement for an earlier generator. It continued in use until the severe winter of 1962-3 when the pressure of ice broke the dam of the lake. At Honeymead, right in the heart of Exmoor, a late installation in 1941 served the whole of the little community. It consisted of twin 9h.p. Pelton wheels (made by Gilbert Gilkes and Gordon of Kendal) each producing 4.5 kW at 700 r.p.m. There were 6in. cast iron pipes to each wheel with an approximate head of 75ft (23m.). The machinery was dismantled in 1965 and only the small turbine house remains.

Paper Making

In the eighteenth century, paper making in West Somerset existed on a very small scale. At Egrove near Williton and at Snailholt near Watchet, paper making was carried on by farmers as a winter occupation for their labourers. William Wood of Snailholt was first recorded in 1750 as a cider and paper maker with seven employees of whom two were skilled – the vat man and the seive man – for paper was still at that time made by hand. The stamps for pounding the rags to pulp were driven by a waterwheel and it is probable that at first the paper was dried on lines in the open, for it was not until later that a drying loft was built over the vat room. Wood made paper for the book trade, selling it on two days a week in Taunton, where he also took his cider. William Wood was succeeded in the business in 1802 by his eldest son, William Jnr and, in about 1820, by his grandson Isaac. In 1816, William Wood Jnr was also the paper maker in charge at Egrove, making paste board as well as paper, but by 1841 Egrove was owned by Robert Pole. Paper ceased to be made there in 1847 when Pole was drowned in the River Parrett when returning from a business journey.

By the time that Isaac had taken over the business at Snailholt, it had moved to a site a few hundred yards down the valley (then owned by the Wyndham estate) which is still occupied by the firm today. Isaac Wood had his own water-mark which can be seen in Hawke's Hymnal, printed in Williton in 1831.

The making of paper succeeded in this locality for three reasons: the ready availability of limestone for burning, for lime was used not only to bleach paper but also to sanitize the rags prior to pulping (these were brought in mainly from the continent and had to be boiled in lime to prevent infection); the quality of water in the Washford river which, being moderately hard, did not produce scum; and the occurrence of Gypsum in the cliffs on the coast west of Watchet which, when ground, was used as a 'loading' material for paper.

After a big fire in 1845, the business was acquired in 1846 by John Wansborough who was a paper maker in Cheddar. He was joined in partner-ship by Peach and Date, who were not only investors but also had knowledge of paper making. Machinery was introduced, first with Robert's continuous webb machine and later by Fourdrinier machines, named after Henry and Sealy Fourdrinier who had perfected the process in 1804. The product also changed – sacking and hemp rope waste were included with the rags and the paper pro-duced was now 'shop browns' wrapping paper and 'coloured blue' for sugar wrap. Lancashire boilers were installed and steam drying of the paper started. The Company employed 25 to 30 men on its 1 acre site. By the end of the century, draught problems were experienced with the boilers and, to overcome this, an underground flue was constructed up the side of the hill and a chimney built at the top near St Decuman's church. The chimney became redundant in 1962 when gas firing was introduced but it is still a landmark today.

By 1868, John Wansborough had gained sole control although for short periods in the years following the firm was known by several names (Wansborough & Peach, Wansborough & Strange and Wansborough & Worrall) until it became a public company in 1896. Captain A. C. Wansborough, John's son, was by this time in control of the firm but he suffered from ill health and took to his bed, neglecting the papermill. He lived at The Elms, Freize Hill,

Taunton and also at Watchet, probably at 'Belmont'. He was a staunch Methodist and insisted that all his employees should attend divine service each morning before work and to this end he erected a chapel within the precincts of the works (this was the corrugated iron or so-called 'tin' church brought down from the old mining village at Brendon Hill). However, such time spent in worship had to be made up each day at the employee's expense!

From the 1880s until the use of gypsum as a 'loading' agent ceased about 1914, there was a separate business within the mill producing it – James Wedlake, Gypsum manufacturers.

During the last years of the nineteenth century, the mill experienced problems, made worse by a disastrous fire in 1898. Although the mill quickly got back to work, with its 100-strong workforce, the problems remained and the firm went into receivership in 1902. In 1903 William Reed, a Devon paper-maker with a mill at Silverton on the River Culm, took over the Watchet mill, with his son Edgar later becoming manager. Previous to the acquisition of the Watchet mill, Reed had for a short period traded with a partner, Smith, and the firm continued under the name of 'Reed and Smith Ltd'. William's son, Albert, went on to found the Reed paper making empire whilst Edgar remained as managing director of the Watchet mill until 1947.

In 1916, the Paper Makers' Union struck for better wages. The strike was eventually settled but Reed closed the paper bag side of the business. The foreman of that department, Mr Pearse, bought the redundant paper bag making machines, renovated Stoate's disused flour mill, and founded the Exmoor Paper and Bag Company remaining, with his son Alan, in business until the mid-1970s. In 1927, a very large 45h.p. Vortex turbine, built and installed by Gilbert Gilkes and Gordon, was installed to power the works and provide it with electricity. It is still in situ.

During both World Wars, straw was used at Wansborough as a substitute for wood pulp but this necessitated the straw being boiled to break down its cellular structure and the resultant effluent fouled the Washford river. In the 1940s, another process was used which eliminated this nuisance but, owing to patent infringements, this had to cease in 1950. In 1950, wood pulp imported from Scandinavia was being used with a little waste paper, and five paper-making machines were producing 250-300 tons of paper per week. By 1967, there were 621 employess on the 6-acre site turning out 450 tons per week. The annual amount of wood pulp used by 1973 amounted to 25,000 tons.

In 1976, the firm was acquired by St Regis International of America but when, a few years later, they decided to shed their British assets, there was a management buy-out, although the name St Regis was retained and the works still called the Wansborough Mill. The mill is now part of the largest paper making group in Britain with a workforce of 300 on a 10-acre site. Using 96% waste paper and 4% wood pulp, it has now two machines – an M.G. (machine glazing) machine making 570+ tons of high quality paper per week for envelopes etc. and a Fourdrinier machine turning out 2000+ tons per week of lining paper for cardboard boxes.

The only other possible site of paper making in the region was at Dulverton where, at the turn of the present century, a building in Lady Street (now demolished) was known as 'the old paper mill'. Nothing more is known of it but in all probability it was an old fulling mill which found another temporary use when the woollen industry ceased.

The Woollen Industry

Of all the past industries of the Exmoor area, none have disappeared so completely as that of woollen manufacture, yet for centuries it was the mainstay of the local economy. Apart from two notable exceptions, the only physical evidence that remains is the legacies of the social effects of the trade – the beautiful churches, such as the one at North Molton, which were 'built on wool', and the many packhorse trackways which crisscross the region. The importance of the latter can be judged by the settlements which grew up at their junctions and by the substantial packhorse bridges which survive, such as Allerford, Brendon, Dunster, Horner and Winsford, and of course Tarr Steps. The prosperity of the junctions, however, declined with the trade – Luckwell (Bridge), for instance, has become little more than a name.

Prior to the thirteenth century, the making of woollen cloth had been confined to the towns and cities of England, but when water-powered fulling stocks were introduced into this country about 1185, they obviated the most laborious labour-intensive and slowest process in the making of cloth – fulling by hand or, rather, feet! However, fulling mills required a plentiful supply of 'quick water' to work them, so they had to be sited in the hilly, wetter parts of the country and it made economic sense for the other processes to follow. The uplands surrounding Exmoor were particularly favourable and fulling mills are recorded at Dunster by 1259 (by the beginning of the fifteenth century, there were four), North Molton by 1314 and Dulverton by 1340, and these little towns were soon prosperous centres of the woollen industry, whose fortunes were assured by the ready availability of wool from the sheep which thrived on these uplands. The industry was not, however, confined to these centres, for fulling mills are known to have been established over a wide area: at Milltown on the River Heddon, Fullaford on a tributary of the River Bray, at Washford, Horner and at Porlock. Here, in a law suit over water rights in 1605, a witness stated

131

'William Fry Esq... had and used to have a certaine tuckinge (fulling) myll and a myll leat derived from out of the same meane streame or watercourse unto the said tuckinge myll...'. These scattered fulling mills were themselves centres for the local population for, as John Hooker, writing in his *Synopsis Chorographical of Devon* in 1599 says:

> There is no market nor village nor scarse any privat mannes house where in theise clothes be not made, or that there is not spynninge or cordinge for the same: as the daylye travellers can so witnes it for wheresoever any man doth travell you will fynde at the hall dore as they do name the fore-dore of the house he shall I say fynde the wiffe theire children and theire servantes at the turn spynninge or at theire cardes cardinge and by wch comoditie the common people do lyve.

Like corn mills, fulling mills generally belonged to the manor or the borough, which collected dues for work done. Needless to say, the Crown was also an owner and in 1608, when trade was flourishing in this region, James I asked Sir Julius Caesar, the Chancellor of the Exchequer, to render account of properties owned. One was a fulling mill on Hunt's Chantry Land at North Molton which produced a rent of 14/- per year.

The making of woollen cloth – at first the coarse cloth known as 'straights' and later, by the end of the fifteenth century, the much finer 'kerseys' – was for centuries a domestic rather than a factory industry but was, nevertheless, a highly organised business and is well described by Westcote in his *History of Devonshire* of 1630:

> First, the gentleman farmer, or husbandman, sends his wool to market, which is bought either by the comber or spinster, and they, the next week, bring that hither in cloth, when it is sold, either to the clothier, who sends it to London, or to the merchant, who, after it hath passed the fuller's mill, and sometimes the dyer's vat, transports it.

The combers produced long hanks or chains – the warp – from long-haired wool whilst the spinsters made the weft from short-haired wool. It was said that eight of these kept one weaver in work.

During both the seventeenth and eighteenth centuries, the Luttrells of Dunster Castle had a hand in trade and commerce and, in 1601, George Luttrell built, in the middle of the main street of Dunster, that unique relic of the wool trade, the beautiful Yarn Market, where tradesmen and merchants could meet and exchange business. In the middle of the eighteenth century, Henry Fownes Luttrell converted a corn mill to fulling – not very profitably, as by that date the woollen trade was in decline.

Gradually, the clothiers and merchants began to employ the tradesmen directly, providing the wool and yarn, hiring the weavers their looms (at 1/- per quarter) and then, to stop the time-honoured practice of the weavers taking enough yarn to clothe their own families, of having the looms in rooms attached to their own houses where the whole process was under their control. Great fortunes were made and dynasties founded. In the early fifteenth century, Thomas Parker was a wealthy merchant in North Molton and here the Parker family built a new house, made prosperous and advantageous marriages and eventually, in 1712, bought Saltram House, near Plymouth, where they were to live as the earls of Morley.

From the very beginning of the trade, the guilds, such as 'The Worshipful Company of Weavers, Fullers and Shearman of the City of Exeter', rigorously controlled the quality of the cloth and the activities of the tradesmen and merchants. However, the government increasingly took a regulatory interest and an Act of Parliament of 1607 decreed that 'every broadcloth commonly called Tauntons, Bridgwaters and Dunsters, made in the western parts of Somerset, or elsewhere, or like making, shall contain, being thoroughly wet, between twelve and thirteen yards, and in breadth seven quarters of a yard at least, and be well scoured, thickened, milled, and fully dried, shall weigh thirty pounds of cloth at least'.

During the seventeenth and eighteenth centuries, the cloth made around North Molton and Dulverton went largely to the merchants at Tiverton whilst Dunster had close links with Minehead. Tiverton was a very large centre indeed having, at one time, 57 fulling mills. Barnstaple by then was in decline, being too isolated from the trading centres. Minehead was the Staple port for North Somerset and it was compulsory for all traders to have their wool and cloth weighed there. For a long time, sufficient wool could not be produced locally to sustain production and large quantities had to be imported. Between 1718 and 1740, 30,000 stones of wool (a stone = 24lbs) were imported annually through Minehead from Ireland alone. In 1714, the traders in Taunton and Tiverton sponsored a petition to have Watchet as the Staple port in place of Minehead but this was vigorously opposed by Madam Luttrell, her trustees and tenants, and the Mayors and Corporations of Taunton, Bridgwater and Bristol and the petition was dismissed.

By this time, the trade had started to decline, largely because of competition from other centres in Yorkshire and Gloucestershire and the introduction of cheap cotton goods. This was exacerbated in North Molton's case by a disastrous fire at Tiverton which disrupted trade. By the end of the eighteenth century, there were only some 200 people employed in the wool trade in and around North Molton, with a similar number at Dunster and some at Dulverton, but it was the Napoleonic Wars which sounded the eventual death knell for the woollen trade in this area.

Kay's invention of the flying shuttle in 1733 led to the gradual development (via the spring loom) of the power loom whilst, later, Arkwright's water frame and Hargeave's spinning jenny completed the simple mechanisation of cloth-making processes. These new machines came to the west and, some time towards the end of the eighteenth century, 'manufactories' were set up at Heasley and at Dulverton, making serges. It was at about this period that the village of Heasley acquired its present name, Heasley Mill. The machinery in the four-storied factory at Heasley Mill was worked by two overshot water-wheels and, at the beginning of the nineteenth century, produced 'long ells' (a type of serge) for the East India Company, which used this cloth as exchange in its monopoly trade with China. In fact, it was only this outlet to the East India Company that enabled the cloth trade to survive in this area, and when the Company's monopoly was broken in 1834, the decline was swift.

At this time, the area around North Molton had four wool staplers, two woollen manufacturers and a serge maker but, a few years later, it was reported that only a little cloth 'of a very inferior quality' was being made and the last manufacturer at Heasley Mill, Edwin Maunder, ceased trading between 1857 and 1861. The last mention of the trade in North Molton is in a lease, taken out in 1841, for a 'weaving shop or house, with other buildings'. However, as the lessee was an innkeeper and the 'other buildings' included a malthouse, it is more than likely that it was that which he required. When this property, known as 'Shapton's Tenement', was sold in 1882, it was still described as a 'weaving shop'. The factory at Heasley Mill was demolished at the beginning of this century, with its site becoming the present village green. One end of the build-ing, however, had been converted into a corn mill and this survived, with one wheel, until it in turn was converted into a dwelling a few years ago.

The substantial three-storied woollen mill in Chapel Street, Dulverton, which survives largely intact, was powered by a large 12ft by 12ft (3.7 by 3.7m.) breast-shot waterwheel and made serges and blankets, but by 1830 this trade had ceased and the building became briefly the crape manufactory of Warden & Company. By 1840 it had become a lace factory belonging to a Henry Smith, but an advertisement of September 1847 reads 'For Sale, Dulverton Silk Mill & Factory. Mills, Factory, Weaving Shop and other erections'. It struggled on under James Booker, a silk throwster of Exeter, until 1871 when James himself was 'out of employ'. From 1880, the building became the carpentry works of Peter Puttock and his son Arthur, and in 1903 part was used by Arthur's wife as a laundry. In 1935, Rodney Peake and his sister Maria installed new laundry machinery and it is still a laundry today.

Mechanisation never came to Dunster and, although Collinson wrote in 1791 that there were still some 190 houses occupied with spinning and weaving, the days of the hand loom were numbered and the trade soon ceased altogether.

Bibliography and Acknowledgements

Annett, N.,	*The Story of North Molton*, MS, 1980.
Binding, H.,	*Discovering Dunster*, 1990.
Binding, H. and Bonham-Carter, V.,	*Old Dulverton and Around* , 1986.
Binding, H. and Stephens, D.,	*Minehead: a New History*, 1979.
Edwards, N.,	'Paper Making at Watchet', *Bull. Som. Ind. Arch. Soc.*, no. 62, 1993, pp.9-12.
Healey, C. Chadwick,	*History of Part of West Somerset*, 1901.
Orwin, C. S. and Sellick, R. J.,	*The Reclamation of Exmoor Forest*, 1970.
Strong, R. W.,	*Industries of North Devon*, 1889, reprinted 1971.
Tucker, D. G.,	'Hydro-Electricity for Public Supply in Britain 1881-1894', *Ind. Arch. Rev.*, Vol. 1 no. 2, 1977, pp.140-7.
Warren, D. W.,	'W.H. Pool and Sons, Engineers, Chipstable', *Som. Ind. Arch. Soc. Survey*, no. 4, 1988.
	'Chidgey's Foundry, Watchet', *Jour. Som. Ind. Arch. Soc.*, no. 3, 1981, pp.6-9.
	'The Kingsbrompton Wagon Works', *Bull. Som. Ind. Arch. Soc.*, no 42, 1986, pp.6-8.
	'John Brayley, Machinist', *Bull. Som. Ind. Arch. Soc.*, no 57, 1991, pp.3-15.

I am particularly grateful to Nigel Edwards for allowing me to use, in its entirety, his article on paper making at Watchet, and to Brian Murless for information on the brick and tile industry around Minehead. I would also like to thank the Local History Library, Taunton, the Somerset Rural Life Museum, Glastonbury, the West Country Studies Library, Exeter, and the North Devon Record Office, Barnstaple.

TRANSPORT

John Bentley
(with a note on the Florence Tramway by Michael Messenger)

Only three modes of transport concern the Exmoor region – seaborne (mostly coastal), railways and roads. Sadly, the first two are now virtually defunct. Wimbleball and Clatworthy in the south-east corner supply water outside the area. Electricity supply and telephone lines are hardly transport and have a minimal impact anyway.

Coastal Shipping and Ports

Coastal trade was always important, particularly as land transport was at best slow, difficult and expensive. There were no large ports but ships were all very small and small boats could be beached in many places, and various small ports developed.

Ilfracombe is too far west for inclusion in the Exmoor area, so this is not the place to dwell on the finer points of its harbour construction. However, the Exchequer Warrant of 1678 gave its port limits as Morte Stone eastwards to the county boundary, just 4 miles from Porlock Weir, so it cannot just be ignored. It was, and long remained, the major harbour on some 27 miles of coast. Much of the local shipbuilding took place on the beach on the south side of Ilfracombe harbour, the entrance being to the east. As with other Exmoor creeks and harbours, trade was chiefly coastal, across to the Welsh ports, and with Ireland, but ships much over 100 tons could not use it, and entry and exit in adverse weather could be difficult or virtually impossible.

Sloops, ketches and schooners seem to have been the main vessels used, and Constant Coasters, carrying both passengers and assorted cargo, called several times a week by the end of the eighteenth century. Imports of Welsh coal were a major feature, as well as limestone and culm for the limekilns which littered the whole coastline wherever unloading was possible.

The first paddle steamer visited Ilfracombe in 1822 and the number of such vessels rapidly increased although few were small enough to enter the harbour. The number of local vessels declined from a peak of just over 120 after 1808, although some shipbuilding in the harbour continued up to the 1860s, no doubt partly because the steamers has no proper facilities – it was not until an Act of Parliament in 1870 that a Promenade Pier was authorised at the harbour entrance so that berthing was possible. Paddle steamers seem to have out-numbered screw steamers, but triple expansion engines were general.

Meanwhile, in 1839, the Board of Customs had reduced Ilfracombe to a mere subsidiary of Barnstaple, and vessels were no longer registered locally. The Barnstaple and Ilfracombe Railway, backed by the L.S.W.R., opened in 1874, and by 1886 the very last steam packet boat was withdrawn. Pleasure steamers had appeared by then and, although the railway probably took some traffic, they remained popular. A number of firms competed, but White Funnel Line was the most successful and ultimately the only survivor. With changes in public tastes, even this firm now has only one surviving vessel, the diesel-engined *Balmoral* – not, of course, of local origin.

Today, Ilfracombe is little more than a yacht marina, but do not forget that manning the lifeboat is the most hazardous but occasionally most rewarding job of all.

Neither **Hele** nor **Watermouth** really qualify as harbours, although a few boats were built at both. Both serviced limekilns and also delivered stores for local use, as well as smuggled goods no doubt.

On the map, **Combe Martin** looks a promising harbour, but in fact was described as 'a poor haven' by Westcote in 1630. If there was ever a quay, it has vanished long since. The main imports were probably coal, both domestic and for the pumping engines at the silver-lead mines, and culm and limestone for the usual limekilns. Exports consisted of agricultural produce, and bark for tan-neries. A few vessels, up to 94 tons, were built on the beach in the nineteenth century but the harbour went out of use in the 1930s. Donn's 1765 map of Devon shows Combe Martin as an important and substantial place, with the road inland built up to for well over a mile, the church being mid-way.

A small inlet north-west of Martinhoe, **Heddon's Mouth** is well hidden and ideal for smuggling, with two substantial hauls being recorded. Otherwise it was only used for servicing the local limekiln, and for the export of pit props to South Wales during the First World War.

The small harbour at **Lynmouth** has twice been destroyed, by storm at sea in 1607, and by torrential floods from the moors in 1952. Its other claim to fame is the dramatic occasion when the lifeboat could not be launched and was hauled overland to Porlock Weir, completing a successful rescue with the aid of two steam tugs. The story is too well known to need detailed repetition here.

Land communication to this isolated spot scarcely existed, so all provisions came by sea, and anything available for export left likewise. Initially, coal and other imports had to be off-loaded onto carts. At the end of the eighteenth century, a substantial quay and pier were built on the west side, although a rough jetty is believed to have been built prior to this. A local benefactor, General Rawden, built a 'Rhenish' tower, carrying a light, near the end of the pier in 1860. This was swept away in 1952 but a replica has been erected.

A substantial herring industry was built up, and oak bark for tanning was also exported, using small locally owned vessels, but this trade ceased soon after the First World War. If any large scale smuggling occurred, it was very successful, as it has virtually no record. Three horses carrying spirits were intercepted at Countisbury in 1832, and a gentleman's yacht was suspected, but nothing was proved.

The old lifeboat house survives on the west side of the creek, but there has been no lifeboat since 1944.

The ancient port of **Porlock** has long ceased to exist. There was a Viking raid in 914, from which few Danes escaped with their lives, but the port then was probably at or east of the Decoy (SS 880477), from which the sea has since receded, as has also happened at Minehead and Dunster. Sparkhayes Lane, a holloway, was probably the main access route, worn down by generations of packhorses.

It is not until 1422 that a Brendon manor court records a gift for the making of **Porlock Weir**, and there was a further gift in 1427 for its repair. The original harbour may still have been in use at least until the mid sixteenth century, but references by Leland and others are not very clear. The present harbour at Porlock Weir is protected by the outer ridge of pebbles piled up by the sea, and a small creek through which a stream flowed was improved in the early nineteenth century. The present quay, warehouses and lock gates, 30ft (9.1m.) wide, were built in 1855. The local limekiln survives, and trade was doubtless similar to that at Lynmouth and elsewhere. Very limited shipbuilding took place, and there was a number of locally owned vessels, the largest being 85 tons, but apparently not after the 1920s. The last cargo of coal arrived in 1950.

Again, typically, it now has yachts in summer and nothing but fishing in winter. Land access, except eastwards to Porlock village, is difficult.

The sea has receded at **Minehead** also, and the early harbour, first recorded in relation to weirage duties in 1380, has disappeared beneath the present town. It was situated where the Bratton Stream flowed into the sea, now the foot of Blenheim Road, and by the end of the fifteenth century was becoming inadequate for increasing trade, so Sir Hugh Luttrell built a jetty to enlarge and protect it.

In 1558, apart from Bristol, Minehead and Bridgwater were the only Bristol Channel ports to have port and customs officials, Minehead seemingly slightly the more important, with more ships recorded in 1543 as being large enough to serve with Henry VIII's navy, the largest being Lady Luttrell's of 100 tons. There were 77 seamen, just over half being at sea. As well as coastal trade, there were some voyages to continental ports and foreign vessels, of course, also visited Minehead. About this time, Minehead had 12 ships suitable for longer voyages, and 20 'barks' for coastal trade. Cargoes were mostly beans, coal, iron, salt, wood and wine, as well as important trading in livestock and wool, mainly with Wales and Ireland. By then, however, the sea was receding, the harbour was exposed to northerly and westerly gales and the estuary was silting up. To make matters worse, a shingle bank formed at the mouth of the creek, and the harbour rapidly declined. Weir Pool, near the wide part of the present Quay Street , was excavated to try to flush out the harbour on the ebb tide, but apparently with little effect.

By 1559, drastic and immediate action to save the port was vital, Thomas Luttrell had taken over what was left of the family fortune and estate from his spendthrift and incompetent brother, Sir John, and could not afford to pay for this, so the local authorities petitioned Queen Elizabeth and were incorporated as a borough, with power a to manage their own port. The borough's failure was absolute, and by 1570 the pier was useless, most trade gone, and they turned to Thomas Luttrell to help them out. He promptly died, and the advisers to his successor, the eleven year old George, were not impressed.

The incorporation charter was withdrawn in 1604, technically because the burgesses had not kept the harbour in repair, and in due course they petitioned to have the incorporation restored, George Luttrell counter-petitioned against this, and in 1609-16 he built a new quay on a new site, which still forms the basis of the present one. In 1620, the harbour formally reverted to George Luttrell. Trade and prosperity increased, and harbour accounts in the mid seventeenth century show that the main trade was with Aberthaw, followed by Bristol and Watchet, and all the ports on both sides of the Bristol Channel, as well as Topsham and Weymouth. There was also regular trade with Ireland and annual fishing excursions to Newfoundland.

Unfortunately, the sea continued to recede and the new harbour was already beginning to silt up by the end of the seventeenth century. A new head to the pier, 120ft (37m.) long, was built in 1705, with a timber framework filled with stones, together with a groyne 100ft (30m.) long to reduce silting. All this cost £2000 even with free timber, but within a few years 'the sea worms had gotten into it,' and a strong stone wall had to be built in 1713 to encase the timber frame. The £700 contract went to Daniel Dennell, but he kept demanding extra money and eventually decamped. The Quaker Alloway family had by then settled in Minehead, and Joseph Alloway took over as supervisor, seeing this and further work to a successful conclusion. Joseph had been married by a priest, and, as was customary, was therefore expelled from the Quakers.

Two years later, in 1715, a storm shattered the sea facing wall, damaged the wharfside in Quay Street and demolished adjoining houses. Harbour repairs and removal of silt and stones continued to be a heavy drain on resources, and various Acts of Parliament authorised charges to be made on shipping. An Act of 1701 authorised a charge on vessels sheltering or anchored in the roads – Sidney and Beatrice Webb, in their voluminous studies, mistook this for an early turnpike act, confusing later researchers (including the writer!). Nevertheless, the period nearly up to 1800 was the most prosperous experienced by Minehead. By 1800, however, the peak was past, the sea was still receding and Ilfracombe had overtaken Minehead as the main port.

The bulk of the trade had been with Wales, particularly Swansea, importing coal, culm for limekilns and livestock. Exports included oak bark for tanning and grain. Early in the eighteenth century, imports of wool from Ireland were large, but the woollen industry declined and this dwindled. Linen cloth and various hides also featured. This was despite the unsettled conditions of the seventeenth and early eighteenth centuries, with Barbary pirates raiding ships and shore, and endless wars in Ireland and on the continent – with lots of privateers – as well as our own Civil War. With wholesale smuggling often aided and abetted by the customs officers, it seems quite surprising that any legitimate trade flourished at all.

The nineteenth century brought almost unrelieved gloom as far as the harbour was concerned. By 1830 there were only five or six vessels belonging to the port, engaged in trade along the coast and with Wales. Exports included grain, malt, bark, timber, flour and leather, with imports being mostly coal, culm and limestone. Some herring fishing continued, but this was barely worthwhile as herring stocks were dwindling, and continued to do so. In 1834, the Port of Bridgwater assumed jurisdiction. A few sloops or smacks carried on until about the turn of the century, after which even these faded out. Shipbuilding finally ceased in 1881.

The White Funnel company built a 690ft (210m.) pier for pleasure steamers in 1901, at which vessels could call at most states of the tide, but this was blown up in 1940 during the invasion scare of the Second World War. Also in 1901, a lifeboat station was built, following the overland trip by the Lynmouth lifeboat referred to earlier. The harbour was closed to shipping in 1947 because of the dangerous shingle bank that had built up at the harbour mouth, but in 1951 this was removed and Mr Luttrell handed the harbour over to the Urban District Council. Pleasure steamers can, of course, only berth now for a short period at high tide; many small boats use the harbour for pleasure in the summer, but fishing is just an amusement for visitors.

There is little left of **Dunster Haven** today to suggest that vessels used to sail up the River Avill almost as far as Dunster Castle, since the sea has receded over the centuries and all has silted up. In 1560, Thomas Luttrell obtained a ruling by the Attorney General that Dunster Haven was not liable for harbour dues in spite of a charter of the previous year which included it within the Port of Minehead.

A century later, silting had reduced its trade to insignificance, and the Luttrells transferred their interest to Minehead, as the nearest practical alternative.

Blue Anchor has a slipway but cannot really be called a harbour, although culm and limestone used to be discharged there. In earlier times, alabaster was dug from the cliffs just to the east, and sent off to be carved into monuments, fireplaces and so forth. Later it was used in paper making, much as Cornish china clay is used nowadays.

The main interest for the present study is that, far from silting up, the foreshore level has been dropping, at least for the best part of two centuries. The first length of sea wall was 6ft (1.8m.) high, with foundations 4ft (1.2m.) deep, and was designed in 1817 by Somerset's first County Surveyor, Robert Anstice, who was also involved in the draining of the Somerset Levels. He was responsible to the County Justices at Quarter Sessions, there being no County Council in those days; but this particular job may have been done privately. The wall was backed by pebbles, over which ran the turnpike road (now the B3191) at the same level as the top of the wall. It was soon breached by storms, and eventually abandoned. In 1899, the County Council tried to abandon the road, but there were legal difficulties, so a new and stronger wall was built over a period of years, beginning with the initial length in 1903. Waves rebounding from the wall scoured away the beach and exposed the foundations, so various expedients were tried over the years, with some initial success, but the level of the foreshore continued to sink, and eventually the beach and sand almost disappeared leaving the underlying soft marl with virtually no protection. A few years ago, an adjacent length of wall near Blue Anchor Hotel, for which the Council was not responsible, was undermined, and collapsed while possible remedial measures were being discussed! Rock armour – large rocks laid against the wall as well as forming groynes – has recently been laid, to the disgust of anglers and holiday makers, and seems likely to lead to some build up of fresh sand.

Watchet was a Saxon burgh which was pillaged and burnt by the Vikings in 888. It had a royal mint from the reign of Aethelred II until the twelfth century.

There were at least three further Viking raids (in 918, 977 and 997), and another is recorded in 988, when most of the raiders were killed, 'the King's armie' counterattacking, possibly from Daw's Castle (an iron age earthwork, probably refurbished). The port later declined, but in the sixteenth century a royal commission still reported that 'small botes have and do use to come in with Salte, wyne, etc.'

A map of the reign of Henry VIII shows a modest harbour able to shelter three ships, and somewhat later maps show a breakwater on the western side. Storm damage was frequent, and £3000 raised by a national appeal, was needed to repair damage in 1658-9. Two hundred years later, another severe storm caused significant damage, and four vessels in the harbour were completely wrecked, whilst a further ship en route to Newport with iron ore was lost with all hands. The contract price for a new harbour, from William Tredwell, was a modest £15,068, the work being carried out in 1861-3. This included a breakwater 390 ft (119m.) long, mainly of wood, and an east pier of 590ft (180m.) in composite stone and wood. As described elsewhere, the export of iron ore was building up at this time, and two railways had reached Watchet – the West Somerset Mineral Railway in 1856, and the West Somerset Railway in 1862, the latter extended to Minehead in 1874 – so the port was busy. Exports, largely of iron ore, averaged 40,000 tons a year from 1873 to 1878, but ore production ceased in 1883 and trade declined. Repairs to the breakwater were delayed, and in December 1900 a gale once more wrecked much of the harbour. Watchet Urban District Council (population under 2000!) was formed to handle this and a tender of £16,183 was accepted from C.H. Walker. The western breakwater, now in masonry and concrete, was completed in 1903, just before another gale breached the east wharf, involving the raising of a further £6000.

Before the First World War, Wansborough Paper Mills was expanding and importing much wood pulp and culm (small coal, as fuel), and a few other cargoes also arrived. After the war, the economic situation was desperate, although the Cardiff Marine Stores Co. rented the west pier for shipbreaking, which helped. The first ship was H.M.S. *Fox* , 4300 tons, which took from 1920 to 1923 to dispose of. Another ship followed, but the firm gave up in 1925.

Until recently, Watchet harbour has continued to operate with fluctuating fortunes, but it is hardly industrial archaeology, even if interesting. Gone are the days of mere coastal trade; more recently there have been ships from Spain, Russia, Iceland and Pakistan among others, with the pleasure boat *Balmoral* still calling during local summer excursions. The port celebrated one thousand years of recorded history in 1988 but the mineral line vanished long ago, and the West Somerset Railway, as preserved, has no goods traffic or facilities, even though there is still a little-used connection to British Rail at Norton Fitzwarren. All goods therefore arrive and leave by indifferent roads.

As the lessee of the east pier has recently gone into voluntary liquidation, the port is closed at the time of writing, but may yet reopen.

Roads

A 'road' is presumably a recognisable track of some kind which is customarily used for the movement of people or goods from one place to another. Historically, it is not necessarily negotiable throughout the year, nor by any wheeled vehicle. As a result of the constraints of enclosed land and the need to negotiate fords or bridges, it will usually acquire a definite width and alignment, but may otherwise move periodically from side to side as paths become worn. All prehistoric ridgeways therefore qualify, and are often flanked by barrows at fairly frequent intervals up on the moors. Traditionally, a Saxon 'herepath', or military road, survives in whole or in part between Raleighs Cross and west of Exford, but parts of the route are uncertain, although the modern road follows the ridge throughout.

Before 1800, travelling any distance along the coast between Watchet and Ilfracombe would almost certainly have been by sea, although a few pack animals would have been used for access to isolated communities and for smuggling. Such bridges as existed would have been too narrow to take a cart, and usually with steeply graded approaches. A writer in the *Gentleman's Magazine* in 1752 observed that a Londoner would no more think of travelling in the West of England for pleasure than going to Nubia, and Exmoor would have been an almost impossible route for much of the year.

In 1675, John Ogilby, encouraged by Charles II, published *Britannia*, with strip maps of all main roads, not necessarily usable by wheeled traffic, and two are relevant. His Bridgwater-Barnstaple road ran via West Bagborough-Elworthy-Raleighs Cross-Brompton Regis (Kings Brompton) and thence via Dulverton and the early Wiveliscombe turnpike (see below) to Bish Mill, and on to South Molton and Barnstaple. His other road ran direct from Minehead to Timberscombe and then followed the original Minehead turnpike nearly to Hele Bridge (east of Dulverton) before veering south-south-east to Bury, Morebath, Bampton and beyond.

Things now become more complex with the advent of County Maps and the old series Ordnance Survey, all at 1in. to 1 mile scale, and Turnpike Trusts. The maps, and other than the O.S. were private ventures – Donn (1765) in Devon, Day and Masters (1782), and also Greenwood (1822) in Somerset. The detail included depended partly on which landowners had subscribed, and partly on which routes were considered by the surveyors as constituting a 'road', e. & o.e. The O.S. paid surveyors per square mile of survey, with predictable results in

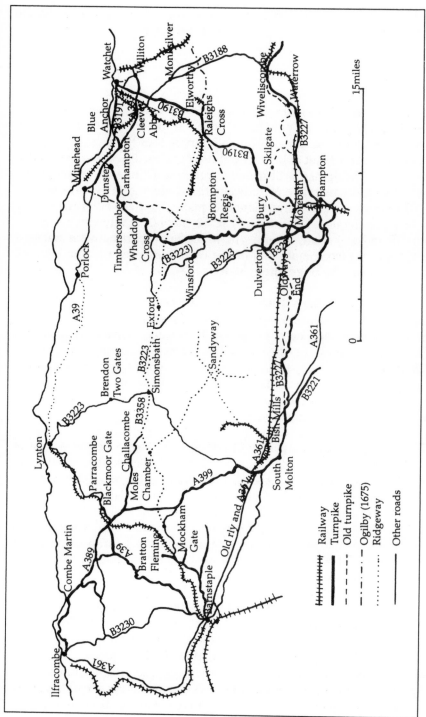

Exmoor's roads and railways.

144

remote areas. Mole's Chamber (SS 717393) on the country boundary, is shown by Day and Masters as a junction of five roads, from all directions (four on O.S.) but Donn shows none, merely noting 'Mole's Chamber a Dangerous Bogg'.

At the end of the seventeenth century, roads throughout the country were in a terrible state. By 1555, there was nobody to maintain them – the Wars of the Roses had impoverished the nobility and county families, and Henry VIII had destroyed the monasteries, seizing their funds and property for his own purposes, which certainly did not include the king's highways. Local parishes were made responsible for the roads in 1555, but without the necessary powers and resources to cope with the problem, statute labour of four (later six) days a year by the minions of the affluent being supervised by a waywarden appointed annually by the parish, with no idea of what to do and how to organise it. Therefore Turnpike Trusts were devised, and were set up, usually for twenty-one years, by Local Acts of Parliament, to collect tolls so that the money could be spent getting the main roads into proper order to hand back to the parishes. Money could be raised on the security of tolls expected to be received. There was no audit and no legal obligation to repair the roads (the parishes still being liable) but as expertise improved, so did the roads – slowly. At the end of twenty years, the roads were still unsatisfactory, so a further Act was obtained (at considerable expense in fees etc.), and this repetition continued indefinitely. After 1815, the soldiers came home, the armaments industry slumped and unemployment shot up, so this was the time for extravagant road building in unlikely places with little regard for the financial consequences. Parliament considered that repayments of debts must take precedence over road maintenance, so tolls were still collected whilst the parishes frequently had to patch up the roads themselves as best they could. This arrangement proved unpopular, and turnpike roads were the worst maintained, so the system was scrapped, some bond holders getting back some of their money, mainly between 1870-1890. The trusts' records were seldom preserved when the roads were handed over to Highway Districts, so the amount of information surviving varies widely.

There were no turnpikes in the middle of Exmoor, but several trusts were involved in the general area.

Minehead Trust (1765-1877) affected the Exmoor area considerably, with four routes:
1) 1765 The old A39 road to Dunster Steep, south of the present line, Carhampton, running straight through the middle of the churchyard, Washford, and then south through Monksilver to Hartrow Gate, ST 901348.
2) 1765 Carhampton (east of churchyard), B3191 to Blue Anchor, Watchet and on to Nether Stowey. The Blue Anchor length, now immediately behind the sea wall, has always given trouble, and still does, as described above under sea-

borne transport. Cliff falls nearer Watchet have resulted in the loss of one stretch, now diverted further inland.

3) 1765 Watchet, B3190 to Bampton. South of Upton, the early route is open to question and could have been further east, via Shillingford, but descriptions are vague and B3190 was certainly used later.

4a) 1765 Dunster Steep (originally via Rattle Row), A396 as far as Timberscombe, Couple Cross, Bury Hill, Hele Bridge, B3222 to Dulverton, Exbridge, Bampton. Timberscombe to Hele Bridge was superseded by 4b.

4b) 1822 New road, now A396, Timberscombe to Exbridge, designed and supervised by William McAdam for a fee of £500, being completed in 1827, but the trust never recovered from the debt incurred. South of Exbridge, A396 was built by the Tiverton Trust.

Wiveliscombe Trust (1786-1871) had just three routes of interest:

1) 1786 Wiveliscombe-Cruwy's Cross-Lowtrow Cross, ST 007292, where it joined Minehead's route 3, above. A short branch, also 1786, ran north from Cruwys Cross to Holcombe Water, ST 057337 perhaps connecting with Ogilby's 1675 route via Raleighs Cross (see above) which ran nearby.

2a) 1786 Wiveliscombe-Waterrow-Raddington Mill-Bury-Hele Bridge, then via the Minehead Trust as far as Dulverton, joining South Molton to Tiverton turnpike at Bish Mill, SS 748254. Beyond Hele Bridge this was part of John Ogilby's Bridgwater-Barnstaple route of 1675 and apparently ran via Upcott, Oldways End and Bullaford to Bish Mill about 2 miles east of South Molton on B3227.

2b) 1806-25 This road, all new except for a length between Bullaford-Bish Mill, was delayed by lack of money, and although authorised earlier, was not built until after the 1825 Act. It ran through sparsely-inhabited country, and was a disaster from which the trust never recovered. The Devon and Somerset Railway followed much the same route in the 1870s with equally discouraging results, showing that some people never learn! Approaching Barstaple, the closed railway is now part of the new A361 road.

3) 1786-1806 Wiveliscombe-Elworthy-Monksilver, now B3188. Not effective north from Elworthy until 1806, then built new.

South Molton Trust (1759) and **Barnstaple Trust** (1763-1879)
Between them, these two trusts altered the road between South Molton and Barnstaple considerably, but had less effect on the area around Exmoor, and that at a much later date. In 1839, the South Molton Trust took powers to build a new road as far as Mockham Gate (SS 665363), now A399, and the Barnstaple Trust's 1841 Act included several straggly roads, the partly new construction, terminating about a mile short of Bratton Fleming village, and also at Loxhore, Horridge and Stone Cross, three miles east of Goodleigh, obviously all local feeder roads into Barnstaple. It had earlier turnpiked, and largely constructed, the present B3230 all the way to Ilfracombe Harbour and, of greater interest in the present context, the A39 route as far as Shirwell Cross (SS 591370).

Combe Martin Trust was not set up until 1838, controlled 17 miles of road, and lasted until 1880. These comprised Combe Martin to Mockham Gate, now the A399 where it met the South Molton Trust; Rowley Cross (SS 662440), south of Parracombe to Shirwell Cross, now the A39, where it met the Barnstaple Trust; Seven Ash to Kentisbury Ford, linking the A399 and A39, now the B3229; and the parish church in Combe Martin to Berry Down Cross on the B3343, (SS 571437).

Combe Martin and Ilfracombe Trust (1865-1889) was a very late trust – the last Devon trust to close – and had just under 5 miles of road, part new construction and part upgraded lanes, now forming part of the A399.

The present coast road, A39, from south of Parracombe, via Lynton to Minehead, was never turnpiked, although a coach ran between Minehead and Lynton, at first in summer only, being first mentioned in *Kelly's Directory* in 1861 without mentioning frequency. New Road, the more easily graded toll road avoiding Porlock Hill, was in use by 1855, when it was referred to in connection with the projected railway from Porlock Weir to Simonsbath.

Historically, bridges were regarded as completely separate structures, with no legal connection between them and adjacent roads. Some are occasionally referred to in Quarter Sessions rolls and old family records but this is of very little help in dating the present bridges since most are comparatively recent, replacing earlier (usually wooden) ones on, or near, the present sites. Older examples, particularly those now wide enough for wheeled traffic, have usually been drastically altered and widened, and where they carry a date stone there is seldom any indication as to whether it refers to initial building, widening, repairing or even merely the conceit of the local lord of the manor. Some stones are so weathered as to be indecipherable. Bridges for which no responsibility could be assigned eventually became County Bridges, administered by the Justices at Quarter Sessions. Turnpike trusts built many bridges, mostly small and of no particular interest.

Once the turnpike trusts were abolished, roads were largely ignored. Highways Districts and County Councils assumed responsibility, but there was little incentive, and less money, to undertake anything beyond basic maintenance. One exception is the road from Brushford to connect with A396, currently forming the southern boundary of the National Park. On the rock face near the west end is a stone:

1895-6 THIS ROAD WAS MADE BY VOLUNTARY SUBSCRIPTION ASSISTED BY THE COUNTY COUNCILS OF SOMERSET AND DEVON. THE LAND WAS GIVEN BY THE EARL OF CARNARVON AND MR P. GOODING.

The names of officers and organising committee follow, but the apparently haphazard variations in size of lettering may not have flattered some! Two new bridges were involved, Perry Barle and Perry Exe, both of which were strengthened in recent times to take modern traffic.

By the 1920s, two things combined to increase interest in roads – the increasing speed, volume and weight of traffic and massive unemployment. Unemployment relief work was introduced by the government, which also provided money, and badly needed road improvements were a good way of tackling the problem. Disillusionment followed, particularly as local government finances could not match the national contributions on offer, causing Winston Churchill to seize the Road Fund for general use by the Treasury, but meanwhile much was accomplished. In Somerset the 'Brendon Road', B3223 and B3224, was breaking up and was comprehensively improved, with a number of new bridges. This included the Coppleham Cross-Winsford-Exford road, at that time classified as the B3223 (the switch to Dulverton-White Cross came later). Works in Devon included the A39, and Parracombe bypass in 1925, while the long and devious detour beside the East Lyn river followed a little later.

Although road making techniques around major cities improved early in the twentieth century, the West Country was understandably slower off the mark. Telford and Mc Adam had refined methods of construction and maintenance a century earlier but water remained a problem, even with good drainage. There was no way of sealing the surface, and wholesale repair was often needed annually. Except for lake asphalt and similar sources, bitumen was not available (although crude oil had been extracted at Kirkuk, now in Iraq, for a thousand years) but coal tar was becoming available from gas works and, initially in a rather crude state, was heated and spread on the road before being covered with small chippings. This produced a far better road needing much less maintenance, and was in use in the West Country by 1908. Use of tar-coated stone in depth followed, with teething problems, about 1925-30. Residual bitumen from oil refineries has now taken the place of tar.

Gordon Home, with advice from the R.A.C., went on extensive tours in a 40h.p. Daimler from 1909, and immediately published *The Motor Routes of England, Southern Section*. In his short preface he says, 'It will be of interest to those who contemplate this tour to know that all the hills, with the exception only of those at Lynton and Porlock, are easily climbable by cars of comparatively low power...' The sections Clovelly to Lynton and Lynton to Taunton are of interest here.

His route from Ilfracombe to Lynton was the A399 to Blackmoor Gate, then the original A39, through Parracombe and straight down Lynton Hill, B3234. 'A good surface, except in the very steep places.' 'Parracombe – very dangerous

148

descent with loose surface, 1 in 7, and ascent of 1 in 9.' 'Lynton to Lynmouth – very dangerous descent of 1 in 5; one of the very worst hills in England.' From Blackmoor Gate, he offered alternatives – 'if a good road irrespective of scenery is desired, the route to Taunton should be taken through South Molton and Bampton. The moorland road to Simonsbath through Challacombe is rough and narrow, and gates are frequent.' His map shows two roads from Parracombe to Lynton, one being the present B3234 and the other passing just west of Dean over the top of the hill.

For Lynton to Taunton, he gave a choice of routes – 1) Lynton-Simonsbath-Exford-Wheddon Cross-Dunster-A39/A358. 2) Lynton-Lynmouth-A39 to Dunster-A396 to Wheddon Cross, Hele Bridge and Bampton-B3227. 3) Lynton -Blackmoor Gate-A399 to South Molton-B3227. Route 1 had a good surface on the whole, excellent from Wheddon Cross, but the road via Raleighs Cross is neither mentioned nor shown on his map. Route 2 included Countisbury Hill, 1 in 7 to 1 in 9, 'and the very dangerous descent of 1 in 6 to Porlock', which is actually 1 in 4 in places and was not tarred until 1933. He mentioned the alternative toll road to Porlock, but not the toll. The road surface was excellent beyond Minehead, and the worst hill was the ascent to Wheddon Cross at 1 in 15. The Rest and Be Thankful Inn at Wheddon Cross and the Luttrell Arms in Dunster both rated mention.

All this was written when the national speed limit of 20m.p.h. had another twenty-one years to run, most traffic (other than bicycles) was horse drawn, and cattle grids would have been quite pointless. Few, if any, of the roads would have been tarred. Lower speed limits applied to some classes of traffic, and Sir George Newnes was heavily fined in 1903 because one of his two steam buses was caught travelling at a little over 8 m.p.h. between Blackmoor Gate and Ilfracombe. The service was promptly withdrawn and the buses sold to the Great Western Railway, which used them between Helston and the Lizard. Perhaps the local police there were more tolerant!

Apart from the roads themselves, many of them widened or realigned since 1920, a large number of milestones survive, together with bridges and toll-houses, but pre-turnpike items are comparatively rare. Old bridges are usually impossible to date, as the sites are older than the present bridges – themselves drastically repaired, widened and strengthened:

Bury Bridge, only 6ft wide, is an Ancient Monument, SS 944274.
Dulverton Bridge carries two plaques recording repair in 1684, and
    widening by John Stone in 1819. Five pointed spans, SS 912278.
Exbridge Bridge, probably eighteenth century, repaired in 1829 by John
    Stone and John Pearse. Three rounded arches, SS 930245.
Landacre Bridge, narrow, with five pointed arches. 'Founderouse and in

Decay' in 1631, but probably rebuilt since. Repaired in 1828, SS 816361.

New Bridge, near Allerford, carries a date stone, 1631 on an upstream buttress. Widened to 16 ft, 1866. Pointed arch plus a half-arch each side for flood relief.

Frackford Old Bridge, derelict, SS 984432. Stone plaque between the two arches records, 'William and George Rawles, masons, 176(?)', perhaps only for repairs. A similar bridge near Dunster Station, with the same names, carries the date 1772, SS 995445. The new Frackford Bridge is an early concrete bridge, built in 1913.

Many Exmoor bridges in Somerset were built in the 1920s when extensive road improvements were undertaken, and blend well into the landscape.

Numerous milestones survive, although sometimes hard to find, with many, but not all, being shown by the Ordnance Survey. Many others, marked on the maps, disappeared long years ago!

Railways

Railways understandably avoided the heart of Exmoor, but those round about were an intriguing mixture, and a few words of explanation will be in order. Brunel's broad gauge reached Exeter St David's in 1844, but the standard gauge London and South Western Railway opened to Exeter Queen Street, now Central Station, in 1860 intending to carry on to Plymouth. After a prolonged dirty tricks campaign it opened, via St Davids, Cowley Bridge Junction and Crediton to Barnstaple in 1854, via nominally independent subsidiary companies. The broad gauge had to get its revenge, but finance for hare-brained projects was hard to come by, so the Devon and Somerset Railway did not open from Norton Fitzwarren, near Taunton, to a separate station at Barnstaple until 1873. In a length of over 45 miles, it managed to avoid all significant centres of human habitation except Milverton and Wiveliscombe, although South Molton was reasonably accessible. Wiveliscombe Turnpike Trust, with a largely parallel route, had come to an inglorious and insolvent end two years earlier. Half a mile east of South Molton station, a tramway from the Florence mine (see below) had a private siding alongside for a few years at the end of the nineteenth century. Not surprisingly, a proposal to upgrade the tramway and extend it to Lynton quietly died. The gauge of the Devon and Somerset Railway was converted in 1881, and a connection to the London and South Western Railway station was built six years later. The Exe Valley line from Exeter connected with the Devon and Somerset Railway at Morebath Junction in 1885. When the line finally closed in 1966, the viaduct south west of Wiveliscombe had reached the end of its life and was beyond economic repair. After closure, the Milverton bypass took over part of the route.

Barnstaple - Ilfracombe

Proposals for a railway to Ilfracombe were made about 1854, when the L.S.W.R. faction reached Barnstaple. All proposals to reach Ilfracombe failed due to opposition from landowners and/or lack of money. although both the L.S.W.R. and the G.W.R. factions were interested, until the Barnstaple and Ilfracombe Railway Company obtained powers to build the line in 1870. The single line encountered engineering problems and both gradients and curves were severe. It was eventually opened in 1874 and the 15 mile line was doubled between 1889 and 1891. The tortuous route was costly to work, the gradients of 1 in 36 and 1 in 40 resulting in three-coach trains being double-headed by two Bulleid 4-6-2 locomotives on occasion. The line survived a little longer than most railways in the area, closing in 1970.

West Somerset Mineral Railway

This line was built by a nominally independent company to serve the iron mines on the Brendon Hills, and opened from Watchet to Roadwater and Comberow in 1857. The Earl of Egremont, as Lord of the Manor, tried to prevent it using the west pier but he proved to have no rights over the public harbour. The West Somerset Railway reached Watchet in 1862 and wanted running powers over the W.S.M.R. for the extension to Minehead (and no doubt to filch some iron ore traffic) but failed, and the two railways were never connected. The railway was leased to the Ebbw Vale Co. Ltd for fifty-five years from 16 June 1864.

Harbour improvements at Watchet were completed in 1862, enabling 500-ton ships to use it. The $^3/_4$ mile incline south from Comberow became usable after a fashion in 1858, but the winding house was not completed until 1859, and it took a further two years to install the 18ft diameter winding drums, these unwieldy objects having been assembled in South Wales, and only transported and installed with great difficulty and delay. Even then, the line did not extend beyond Raleighs Cross, and only reached Gupworthy in 1864. Further extension was considered but abandoned.

Track consisted of assorted short lengths of flat bottomed iron rail, nominally 72lb/yd, laid in cast-iron chairs (except on the incline) which were secured to wooden sleepers by wooden trenails. When Captain Tyler of the Railway Inspectorate, inspected the line in August 1864, he considered trenails to be inadequate, and some iron spikes were added below the incline. Although up to four passenger, or mixed, trains per day ran between Watchet and Comberow from September 1865 (some not carrying third class), no official service was ever attempted up or above the incline, although stations were built at Brendon Hill, (ST 022343), Luxborough Road, (SS 983354) and at Gupworthy (SS 967353). However, passengers were carried at their own risk in open trucks with rough seats both up the incline and on to Gupworthy. Until the Light Railways Act of 1896, all passenger lines were required by law to be built and operated to main line standards, and the lower section should have complied with such increasingly stringent requirements as fully interlocked points and signals, continuous (vacuum) braking and absolute block working, with a staff carried by the driver: up to a point, some compliance was eventually achieved, but maintenance of track and rolling stock deteriorated to vanishing point. A minimal passenger service continued after the mines closed, and materials continued to be salvaged from the mines for some years, together with a little general goods traffic. In 1890, an empty carriage was derailed due to the inner side of the railhead having been worn away completely for several feet – apparently not an isolated problem! The old wrought iron rails were presumably second-hand when installed, and by now required urgent replacement. The tyres of the remaining locomotive and carriages were worn so thin as to cause concern and other considerable repairs were needed. An arch under the incline was on the point of collapse. The railway struggled on until November 1898, when the Ebbw Vale Co. was at last permitted to close it, although it still had to be maintained. Such rolling stock as the G.W.R. would accept was taken back to South Wales, the remainder being broken up at Watchet except for an 0-4-0 tank loco which was removed later. When the mines were in full production, there had been two 0-4-0 T locos on the upper section and two 0-6-0T locos between Watchet and Comberow, but latterly only one of each had been retained.

In 1907 the Somerset Mineral Syndicate recommenced mining in the Brendons. It leased the line from Watchet to Brendon Hill, and also laid a 2ft gauge tramway from West Colton adit (ST053348), via Raleighs Cross to Brendon Hill, largely running along the roadside. The iron ore jetty at the west pier had been destroyed by a gale in 1900, and a new timber jetty was built in 1908. An ex-Metropolitian District Railway condensing 4-4-0T loco was acquired, which could barely negotiate the sharp curves, and damaged both itself and the track. This ill-starred venture staggered on for a while, but collapsed in 1909.

Automatic train control was tested and demonstrated by an Australian firm, A.R. Angus Ltd, on the line between Watchet and Washford, using a system somewhat similar to that already being installed by the G.W.R., this continuing from December 1911 until 1914. The rails were commandeered for scrap by the Ministry of Munitions in 1917, but the Ebbw Vale Company's lease was still in force until 1919, although the railway no longer existed. Sorting things out dragged on until the W.S.M.R. (Abandonment) Act received the Royal Assent in August 1923.

Taunton - Minehead - West Somerset Railway

Like the Taunton-Barnstaple line, the Taunton-Minehead line also diverged from the main line at Norton Fitzwarren. It was promoted by two different independent companies, both broad gauge. The West Somerset Railway with the broad gauge bridge rail laid on longitudinal timber baulks, ran as far as Watchet, opening in 1862, with Brunel having nominally been in charge of construction. The main idea was to cream off some of the iron ore traffic from the Brendon Hill mines, but the W.S.M.R., largely financed by the Ebbw Vale Company of South Wales, refused all co-operation, and the company had to look elsewhere for traffic. This involved extending the pier of Watchet Harbour to accommodate other shipping, and the prospects were not good. In spite of intervention by Henry Fownes Luttrell of Dunster Castle, who had interests in Minehead Harbour, the W.S.M.R. was not interested in further investment, and the Minehead Railway, from Watchet, was financed independently, laid with cross-sleepered track, and after more financial problems opened in 1874. The whole line was converted to standard gauge eight years later. It soldiered on, with mixed fortunes, until 1971, most of the length being revived as a preserved line, in sections, from 1976.

Minehead station is half-a-mile short of the harbour, but by the time the railway opened little seaborne trade remained. A rail siding along the sea front would not have been appreciated by the holiday trade, and no connection was ever made.

Lynton and Barnstaple Railway

Barnstaple had acquired a railway terminus in 1854, but the 1ft 11^1/$_2$in. (60cm.) gauge link to Lynton did not materialise until forty-four years later, for sound economic reasons. Lynton and Lynmouth were of very little importance, no turnpike trust had ever ventured near, and the small harbour promised little trade and bad communications inland. The small settlement of Parracombe was of greater importance in the nineteenth century, but toward the end a small holiday trade showed signs of developing.

The narrow gauge facilitated sharp curves and modest standards. Construction was estimated to cost £2500 per mile for the 19^1/$_4$ mile route, ending 700 ft (213m.) above sea level, very inconveniently for goods and passengers as it was 250ft (76m.) above Lynton itself. Construction actually cost double the estimate, so finance was always desperately short, and the contractor was bankrupted as well. The main engineering feature was Chelfham Viaduct, whose arches still survive, but it was the cuttings through hard rock which did most to enhance construction costs.

The railway was sold to the newly-formed Southern Railway in 1923, and various improvements were put in hand. Speeds were very low, the journey taking one-and-a-half hours, an average of 13m.p.h. so growing competition from road traffic soon made the railway even less economic, particularly as significant improvements were made to the A39, and holiday traffic on this charming line could not finance it on its own. A final conference in Barnstaple, held in 1935, when nearly all protesters arrived by car, guaranteed closure forthwith! Rolling stock was sold as scrap, except for one locomotive, which crossed the Atlantic and disappeared from view. There is a small museum in the signal box of the old Barnstaple Town Station.

The Florence Tramway

The Florence Mining Company Ltd was incorporated in 1871 to exploit a mining lease granted by Lord Poltimore in 1870 to Sidney Hawkins of London. The need for good transport facilities was recognised at the outset and in April 1873 a start was made connecting the mine to the then constructing Devon and Somerset Railway. The 4-mile long Florence Tramway was engineered by George Bush, of George Nympton, and opened in February 1874.

The nearby Bampfylde Copper Mining Co. Ltd saw the advantage of the tramway and in October 1873 commenced building their own connection to it. Disputes between the two companies prevented Bampfylde using the tramway until the following October, however. Production of the two mines varied but several thousand tons of iron ore travelled down the tramway over several years.

Bampfylde went into liquidation in 1878 and Florence in 1879, but were resurrected within a few months respectively, as the North Molton Mining Co. Ltd and the New Florence Mining Co. Ltd. The Bush family were prominent in the latter and evidently raised additional capital. A steam locomotive was bought for the tramway from John Fowler of Leeds in 1880. It was one of a batch built to 2ft 6in. (76cm.) gauge tramway. For three years output from Florence was at least 5000 tons a year but dropped off to 1500 tons in 1883. Liquidation was staved off by raising further capital but production was now negligible and winding up came in 1886. The company's successor, the North Devon Mining Co. Ltd, achieved little and was struck off in 1891.

The steam locomotive was returned to Fowlers at some time and regauged to 2ft 8in. (81cm.). It reappeared in the Isle of Purbeck, Dorset, in 1889 where it remained until 1934. The tramway was, no doubt, out of use by the end of the 1880s.

Little remains of the tramway bar its earthworks and these can now be traced for most of its length. At the south end, at the junction with the erstwhile

Taunton to Barnstaple line, the lines of the sidings are quite clear and the depression of the pit that marks the site of the engine shed can be found. Along the line, traces of bridges are evident across small streams and, just south of the road crossing east of North Molton, across the River Mole. Below Brinsworthy Bridge the earthworks of the junction with the Crowbarn branch are very clear. There is little at the Bampfylde terminus but at Florence there are signs of loading ramps and other buildings among the remains of the mine itself.

Lynton - Lynmouth Cliff Railway

This operates on the system usually employed for cliff railways, the two cars being connected by cable, and a water tank installed under each. The tank at the top is filled until the weight can set the whole in motion. On reaching the bottom, water is discharged, and the other tank filled to repeat the process. As the gradient is 1 in $1^3/_4$, efficient braking arrangements are essential! The gauge is 3ft 9in. (1.14m.), and the two tracks are very close together except for the central passing place where they diverge. The company was set up in 1885 and the railway opened five years later, initially intended mainly for goods traffic, but with removable passenger accommodation, which is still the case. It is the only surviving railway in the Exmoor region, except for the preserved Minehead line. As with other forms of transport, the chief problem is frost – anti-freeze not being a practicable solution!

Minehead - Lynmouth (Projected)

No sooner was the narrow gauge Lynton and Barnstaple Railway completed in 1898 than a scheme for another line, also 1ft $11^1/_2$in. (60cm.) gauge, to link Minehead with Lynmouth was proposed, relying on the hope of reviving the fortune of Minehead harbour and developing the seaside resort generally, so presumably it would have provided a scenic pleasure trip in the summer months, but precious little else. It would have started at the harbour, run along the sea front and past the existing railway station before swinging right round and making for Porlock. It would then have climbed up onto the moors with extensive views, to terminate on high ground above Lynmouth. Minehead pier was, in fact, built in 1901 to accommodate pleasure steamers, but the railway was bitterly opposed by the landowners affected and the scheme lapsed.

Porlock - Simonsbath (Projected)

Frederic Knight attempted unsuccessfully to exploit the iron ore on his large estate centred on Simonsbath and entered into an agreement in 1855 with the Dowlais Iron Company. The Knight estate would build a railway from near Simonsbath to Porlock Weir, whilst the Dowlais Company would provide rails and ironwork. By 1859, mining had ceased, and the mining lease was terminated, but the railway agreement was apparently still in force. Frederic Knight tried to persuade the Dowlais Company to supply the rails, and commenced rather half-hearted earthworks, but apparently with no serious intention of completing the line. Much of the route can still be traced, but the only significant earthwork is a cutting running north from the toll road at SS 853466 towards Westcott.

Today

Linear remains of railways generally fade away by degrees, and space precludes a blow-by-blow account of what remains, so comment will be brief.

The Devon and Somerset Railway is mostly traceable, but the Milverton Bypass (B3227) runs along the formation for most of its length, and the North Devon Link (now A361) does likewise approaching Barnstaple. Dulverton Station, now a private house, is quite impressive, as is Barnstaple Town Station, with its signal box museum.

The W.S.M.R. formation is largely intact, with a public footpath part way between Washford and Watchet. Roadwater to Comberow is now a minor road. The incline is somewhat overgrown and it is far less striking than it was, but the remains of the winding house at the top are clearly visible from the road, set into the embankment. The W.S.R., now a preserved railway, is well worth a visit, but quite a lot of things post-date the original closure.

The L.&B.R. also survives in many places. Chelfham Viaduct (SS 610356) is easily viewed from the road. Barnstaple Town Station has been mentioned already. Blackmoor Gate Station is now a hotel/restaurant, but is just about recognisable.

Bibliography

Bentley, J. B. and Murless B. J., *Somerset Roads, the Legacy of the Turnpikes*, Somerset Ind. Arch. Soc., 1985 (further notes in Phase 2, 1987).

Binding, H. and Stevens, D., *Minehead, a New History*, 1977.

Farr, G., *Ships and Harbours of Exmoor*, 2nd Edn, 1974.

Home G., *The Motor Routes of England*, Southern Section, 1909.

Kanefsky, J., *Devon Tollhouses*, 1976.

Madge, R., *Railways Round Exmoor*, 3rd Edn, 1988.

Mold, E., *Lynton and its Coast*, 1992.

Norman, W. H. (Ben), *Tales of Watchet Harbour*, 1985.

Orwin, C. S. and Sellick, R. J., *The Reclamation of Exmoor Forest*, 1970.

Sellick, R., *The West Somerset Mineral Railway*, 1962.

Vancouver, C., *General View of the Agriculture of the County of Devon*, 1808, reprinted 1969.

Waters, B., *The Bristol Channel*, 1955.

Wedlake, A. L., *A History of Watchet*, 1955, 2nd Edn, 1973.

Periodicals

Kanefsky, J., 'Turnpike Trusts in East Devon, v Railways', *Trans. Devon Ass. Advant Sci.*, 109, pp.59-72, 1977.

Lowe, M. C., 'The Turnpike Trusts in Devon and their Roads; 1753 - 1889', *Trans. Devon Ass. Advant Sci.*, 122, pp.47-69, 1990.

Ridler, J. K., 'The Exmoor Packhorse', *Exmoor Review* Vol 2, 1960.

Rogers, W. H., 'Barnstaple Turnpike Trust', *Trans. Devon Ass. Advant. Sci.*, 74, pp.139-167, 1942.

Spong, H. and Stone, V., 'The Port of Watchet', *Ships Monthly*, June 1989.

Stevens, D., 'Watchet and Porlock', *West Somerset Arch. & Nat. Hist. Soc. News*, 21.

Stevens, D., 'Minehead', *West Somerset Arch. & Nat. Hist. Soc. News*, 22.

Stuckey, D., 'Transported with Joy?', *Exmoor Review* Vol 19, 1978.

Stuckey, D., 'No More Campbells are Coming!', *Exmoor Review*, Vol. 24, 1983.

Thomas, D. L. B., 'Devon's Bridges', *Trans Devon Ass. Advant Sci.*, 124, pp.175-206, 1992

Walden, H., 'Beast of Burden', *Exmoor Review*, Vol. 13, 1972.

SELECTIVE INDEX

159